CALM:
Choosing to Live Mindfully

To Saundra,
May you be free from
suffering and know
great joy!
In lovingkindness,
[illegible]

To Saundra -
May you live with
ease.
In loving-kindness,
[illegible]

CALM

Choosing to Live Mindfully

Angela Buttimer
Dennis Buttimer

Disclaimer

The information in this book is based on professional research and work, as well as the personal views of the authors. This book is not intended as a substitute for the advice of your medical physician or other health care provider. The authors do not prescribe the practices in this book as a replacement for medical assessment, treatment or consultation. This book is not meant to be a compendium of all current research with respect to health and wellness. Any adverse effects incurred, directly or indirectly, from the contents of this book are solely the responsibility of the reader. The authors assume no responsibility or liability for the actions of the reader.

The names and identifying characteristics of clients have been changed or represent an amalgam of various people.

The intent of the authors is to share professional and personal information about mindfulness in a practical way that enables the reader to gain greater health and wellness, and to live a more peaceful, poised, and powerful life.

CALM: Choosing to Live Mindfully
Angela Buttimer
Dennis Buttimer

ISBN-978-0-615-50586-2

Dedication

This book is dedicated to

Scharlene ("Charly") Annette Peterson, who brought much light and love into the world with her dancing eyes, illuminating smile, playful spirit, and contagious laughter

Mary Louise Buttimer, who inspired the best in others, shining her light brightly through kindness, selfless service and devotion

Ronald George Riddle, who was a back-door bodhisattva, quietly offering what little he had to strangers in need, always able to make us smile with his quick wit and humorous perspective on life.

Acknowledgements

To our teachers, Peggy Rowe-Ward and Larry Ward, authors of Love's Garden: A Guide to Mindful Relationships, who are both wise and compassionate, who have been a light for us in the darkness, and whose bodhichitta is a poignant example to us of inner strength and loving-kindness. To you both, we offer a deep bow.

To our friend and colleague, Scott Matthews, who has supported and cared for us through trials and triumphs, who can make us laugh harder than anyone we know, and who generously and tirelessly offered his time, energy, and commitment to excellence in helping us edit this book.

To our friend and colleague, Carolyn Helmer, Manager of Cancer Wellness at Piedmont Hospital, for whom we have deep respect and gratitude, for her visionary leadership, support and encouragement, her unwavering belief in our talents and abilities, and her steadfast availability to share feedback and insights.

To our friend and colleague, Dr. Jody Iodice, author of Sit Up in Your Truck and Smile, for being our cheerleader, our comrade and playmate, for her willingness to laugh and cry with us as we behold the absurdity of life, and for encouraging us throughout the writing of this book.

To our friend and colleague, Chef Nancy Waldeck, author of Taste and Savor: Delicious Healthy Recipes & Tasty Wine Tips, for her unwavering enthusiasm for our teachings, her generosity and willingness to share resources and fabulous food, and the inspiration and chutzpa she has provided as a fellow entrepreneur with her pioneering spirit, lighting the way.

To Nancy Sherrill for her creativity and fortitude in designing the cover and layout of this book, and for her patience and flexibility as we re-negotiated deadlines.

To Robert M. Brown for providing outstanding service in creating our integrative health and wellness blog, www.allthingsintegrative.com.

To Jennifer Louden, author of The Life Organizer: A Woman's Guide to a Mindful Year, our writing coach, who guided and encouraged us in our writing practice.

To our friends and colleagues at Cancer Wellness, our home away from home, who have supported us through some of our darkest days – John, Carolyn, Jody, Nancy, Cindy, Jackie, Tallulah, Barbara, Edna, Rebecca, Amy, Shayna, Gillian, Sarah, Beci, Hans, Mary Nell, Lea, Tyler, Daniel, Tavari, Julie, Kim, Tawanya, Arrington. How fortunate we are to be a part of such a professional, inspired, talented and like-minded group!

To the many friends and family members who have cheered us on along the way, checking in periodically, with ever-so-slight pressure, asking us "WHEN is your book coming out?"

To the many dharma teachers and elders who have paved the way-from whom we have learned and been inspired-we offer a deep bow of gratitude.

To our parents, for supporting us in our meditation practices at an early age and the intellectual freedom to explore various philosophies.

To Kevin and Justin, our sons, of whom we are immensely proud, who model loyalty and steadfastness and continue to delight us in their creative endeavors, and who embody the noble qualities of goodness and authenticity.

To Christian, Savannah, and Lana, our precious nieces, three of the most compassionate young people we have encountered, who delight us with their youthful female perspectives of the world, who remind us to practice "beginner's mind" and to keep an open heart.

To Jacob, our amazing nephew and godson, who reminds us to laugh, play, and take ourselves lightly, who provides us with a great model for being fully present and accessing our inner two-year olds, and who opens our hearts wider than we ever imagined possible.

To one another, for seeing the best and the beauty in each other, even when life is not coming up roses; for providing sanctuary during difficult times, and practicing unconditional love and acceptance along the way. It is a one-of-a-kind love.

And most importantly, to our many clients and students over the years, to the Cancer Wellness community, especially to the sacred Thursday morning sangha; to the many boddhisattvas who have trusted us to lead and guide them on this journey, who have taught us in return, who have shared openly and courageously, who have inspired us with their willingness and fortitude to heal and transform their lives. We are deeply humbled and touched that you chose to be on this path with us. Each of you has impacted us in profound ways, and we treasure your presence in our lives.

Foreword

Our teacher, Zen Master Thich Nhat Hanh, often describes mindfulness practice this way. Every minute of every day we have many conditions for happiness. Without mindfulnesss we can overlook our opportunity to be in touch with them. We breathe in and we breathe out and we forget to notice that each breath is a miracle. The clouds are in the sky, our oak tree is out front, and children are laughing in the park. It is so easy to miss our precious appointment with our own life.

This forgetfulness is an old habit. Which is why the heart of mindfulness is remembering. You might ask, "Remember what"? Remember that we have this one precious life. Remember that we are alive. You've seen information maps that have the big arrow denoting "You Are Here". That arrow is right over our head. Here we are. This is it!

Practicing mindfulness invites us into the present moment. Breathing in, knowing that we are breathing in, and breathing out, knowing that we are breathing out, we can touch the calm and the peace that can reside in every cell of our body. It is so very simple. And yet, our personal and collective habit energy can make this a challenge.

It is a wonderful gift to be able to taste the present moment. Our modern society encourages us to hurry, to run after things and even to multi task. Some of you may have had the experience of waking up in the morning and already feeling that you are behind. We know that we have had this experience of busyness and it can be heart killing.

This book is a wise and gentle guide to assist us in slowing down to the speed of life. Angela and Dennis are compassionate cultivators of mindful living. They have collected some of the teachings of the Buddha that are over 2,600 years old. The ancient teachings are illustrated with stories from their own lives and the lives of their family, friends and clients.

CALM: Choosing To Live Mindfully offers practical tools that will help you to practice mindfulness and to invite calming into your daily life. This will enable you to generate the kind of energy that will help you to taste the wonders of life.

As we imagine our friends Angela and Dennis holding this book before us, we are reminded of a quote from Mother Teresa. She acknowledged that "I am a little pencil in the hand of a writing God who is sending a love letter to the world". CALM: Choosing To Live Mindfully is being sent to us as one of those love letters. We invite you to open it.

Blessings on all of our wise and wonderous lives.

May all beings be happy, safe, healthy and at ease.

Dr. Peggy Rowe Ward and Larry Ward

Dharma Teachers in the lineage of Thich Nhat Hanh,

Authors of Love's Garden: A Guide To Mindful Relationships

Table of Contents

Introduction 2
Today is a New Day 5
The 4 C's of Mindfulness 8
The Present Moment 12
The Four Noble Truths 16
Three Roots of Suffering 20
Ego, Attachment, and Suffering 23
Loving-Kindness 26
Compassion 37
Joy 44
Equanimity 49
The Wisdom of Impermanence 55
Working with our Thoughts 60
Working with our Emotions 66
Working with our Bodies 72
Self-Love, Self-Honor, Self-Compassion 78
Mindful Relationships 86
Grief 91
Forgiveness and Internal Knots 96
Generosity 102
Right Effort 107
Mindful Consumption 111
Humor and Mindfulness 115

Spirituality....119
The Way of the Boddhisattva....123
We're all in this Together....128
A Call to Action....131
Practices....136
References....153
Recommended Resources....163
About Cancer Wellness at Piedmont....172
About The Authors....174

Introduction

Dear Readers,

Thank you for taking the time to read our book. We are honored that you are giving your valuable attention to this work, and we hope it will provide a fresh perspective as you navigate the 10,000 joys and 10,000 sorrows of life.

We wrote this book to give readers exposure to mindfulness teachings through the door of Buddhist psychology. These ideas are not original. As is said in these teachings, "there is no original idea." We bring our own unique perspectives and experiences, both personally and professionally, to these ancient concepts.

This book is designed as a guide for those wanting to learn about mindfulness, for those seeking to reinforce their practice, and for those wishing to refresh their perspective. Our goal is to make the information as accessible as possible, to a wide array of readership, who may be approaching these teachings from different walks of life.

We have included journaling questions at the end of each chapter as a way for you to explore and apply these concepts personally. You will find added value and a deepening of your understanding by writing your thoughts, feelings, insights, observations, and experiences rather than simply thinking about them. When you write, you grow in both clarity and wisdom. As a way to further integrate concepts from each chapter, we have also included suggested practices at the end.

We have kept the chapters relatively brief given modern day time and energy constraints. In our busy lives, time is one of our most valuable commodities. Each chapter is intentionally self-contained, so you can choose where you would like to begin. *We have highlighted our personal experiences in italics throughout the book to distinguish between the personal "we" and the collective "we."*

We applaud you for taking some time for your personal growth. Much healing can occur when we take time for self-reflection and contemplation, cultivating a deeper relationship with ourselves.

In the "Practices" section, we have outlined some experiential exercises. We have CDs available to lead you through these practices if you prefer spoken guidance. We have also listed many references, for both reading and listening, at the end of the book. You may resonate more with some of the practices than others. Start where you like and incorporate other practices as you are ready.

The research we have included in this book is just the tip of the iceberg. New research is published daily on the benefits of mindfulness practice. Check our blog, www.allthingsintegrative.com, for updated information.

We would like to share a classic Zen tale that captures the journey and benefits of mindfulness.

A great samurai comes to a Zen master and says, "Tell me the nature of heaven and hell."

The Zen master looks at him with disdain and says, "You don't look like a samurai. You look like a beggar to me."

Enraged, the samurai draws his sword and raises it to cut off the master's head. The Zen master says, "That's hell."

Seeing that his anger was indeed hell, the samurai calms down, bows in gratitude, and thanks the Zen master for sharing his wisdom.

"And that," the Zen master says with his arms wide open, "is heaven."

In loving-kindness,

Angela and Dennis

1

Today Is A New Day

"We can live our lives as if nothing is a miracle
or as if everything is a miracle."
–Albert Einstein

Everyday, we have the opportunity to begin again. Each day as we arise, we can be grateful for just that - the gift of another day, something we often take for granted. We have the opportunity to do something different today, perhaps simply choosing to be grateful...grateful that our eyes can see and our lungs can breathe. As tempting as it is to assess our needs and complaints as we face our day, we find that a focus on gratitude creates the springboard for a miracle-filled day.

When retreating with teachers Peggy and Larry, at each sunrise meditation, Peggy begins with "Today is a new day." She rings the mindfulness bell, and we meditate together. Her statement is a profound one as we allow the miracle of its truth to permeate. This doesn't mean that we become whole new selves, or that our lives change with the sunrise. It does mean that we have the opportunity to make better choices, think about things in a more empowering way, and commit to correcting the mistakes of yesterday. We miss the gift in this awakening if we are stuck in the past or the future. Regret and worry derail our good intentions to live in the present with an open heart, clear mind, calm body, and connected spirit.

We may still carry the same grief or bad news from months earlier. As we explore the subtleties and nuances of this insight, we find that our approach to these old subjects can shift, expand, and alter. You may not be ready to open the door wide on this truth, so give yourself permission to just crack the door open, allowing some light in to glimpse this reality.

Today is not the same as yesterday, and we are not the same as we were yesterday. We, and life, and everything and everyone in it, are much more fluid. We often attempt to concretize the world as a way to understand and control, but this is an illusion. Recognizing the truth of fluctuations in all things, in each moment, helps us embrace the newness of each day.

In her book Start Where You Are: A Guide to Compassionate Living (2001), Pema Chodron reminds us that, not only does each day bring the possibility of starting over, each moment provides this as well. We may be halfway through our day when we wake up to being derailed. In this moment, we can begin again, right where we are. We can awaken to this hopeful message, full of possibility. We can choose how we want to influence our lives, and we can begin again as often as necessary. We also find this in our meditation practice. When "monkey mind" creeps in, once we become aware of it, we begin again by focusing on our breath and good intention. Some days we find ourselves starting over many, many times. We encourage you not to become frustrated. This is why we call it a "practice." Pema also reminds us that aspiration and action are both valuable. When we are unable to manifest our intentions as actions, living with our aspirations helps us take turtle steps towards eventual right action.

Earlene, a sangha member at Cancer Wellness at Piedmont, often delights us with her rich stories of applied insights. Recently she described an encounter with a truck driver on the road. He nearly ran her off the road, and she began yelling in anger. When she awoke in the moment to what she was doing, she immediately shifted into phrases of metta (loving-kindness) still shouting loudly, "***Truck driver, may you be held in loving-kindness!!!***...and so on." Earlene and her passenger laughed heartily, and so did the sangha upon hearing her story.

Self-Reflection

Take a moment to write about the statement: "Today is a new day."

What does that mean to you?

What are your aspirations for today?

Practice

Upon waking each day, say to yourself "Today is a new day."
Approach your day with freshness and curiosity.
Throughout the day, begin again, as needed.

2

Four C's of Mindfulness

"Turn your wounds into wisdom."
-Oprah Winfrey

Approaching life's difficult situations can be intimidating for any of us. Using a roadmap or a compass can help. We have found this assistance in what we like to call the four C's:

Calm

We decided to entitle this book "CALM" because in our experience, this quality must take the lead. If we are not in a place of equanimity, we cannot access our compassion and clarity or make empowered choices. When we create a calm spaciousness within, compassion and wisdom arise organically. We all seek peace and yet, as Gandhi has suggested, "We must be the change we wish to see in the world." If we want peace, we must bring a calm presence into all situations. Mindfulness practice helps us to do this.

Compassion

Compassion reminds us to keep our hearts open. Even when we disagree with someone or something, we can remain receptive to them. Holding ourselves with compassion is equally important. With an open heart, we cultivate more joy, love, kindness, generosity, and patience. Compassion is both soft and strong. Mindful compassion is backed by wisdom and equanimity. Mindless compassion, in contrast, is often led by an unconscious or habitual tendency to enable others. Discernment is central to mindful compassion practice.

Clarity

With an abiding calm and an open heart, we act with clarity. Clarity is aligned with acceptance and wisdom, our commitment to cut through self-deception, to see things as they really are. Clarity calls for both courage and letting go. This is the essence of the mantra "Om Mani Padme Hum" meaning that wisdom and compassion are inherent within us and arise naturally when we commit to walking the path of mindfulness. The Dalai Lama reportedly chants this mantra daily as part of his meditation practice. Our sangha at Cancer Wellness (Piedmont Hospital) wears mindfulness beads engraved with this mantra. This tangible symbol reminds us of this mantra's truth and our commitment to our practice.

Choice

In taking personal responsibility for the lives we are leading and creating, we realize our inherent power. Although much in life is beyond our control, our reactions and choices are within our control. By responding more skillfully, we can choose to change habitual reactionary patterns that cause suffering. Whatever we choose, we strengthen that quality within ourselves and in our lives. Each day, and even in each moment, we can choose calm, compassion, and clarity, or we can indulge in the seductive energies of the world, thus creating a frenetic, competitive, and chaotic environment within and around us.

Many of us were not taught how to embody and express these attitudes. How do we bring calm to an experience we fear? How can we be compassionate in the face of anger or jealousy? How do we find clarity when feeling overwhelmed and torn? Through practice, we can find calm in the midst of the storm.

Formal mindfulness training consists of three practices: guided body scan, sitting meditation, and mindful yoga. Informal practice consists of developing self-awareness and making behavioral changes. Informal practice includes fostering attitudes and insights we learn from studying, contemplation, and behavioral implementation. The combination of formal and informal practice leads us to feeling more peaceful, powerful, and poised in the world.

We bring these teachings to you primarily through the door of psychology. In this way, we have chosen to follow the lead of Dr. Jon Kabat-Zinn, author of Full Catastrophe Living: Using the Wisdom of Your Body and Mind to Face Stress, Pain, and Illness (1990), and Coming to Our Senses: Healing Ourselves and the World through Mindfulness (2005), a molecular biologist at University of Massachusetts Medical Center. Jon has been a pioneer, bringing these teachings to mainstream America, originally through the healthcare system. He saw the great benefits possible for our health and has since been responsible for leading much of the current research. Benefits of mindfulness practice include, but are not limited to: enhanced immune functioning, reduced inflammation, reduced pain and improved ability to manage chronic pain, improved anxiety and depression symptoms, regulated blood pressure, improved sleep patterns, and greater happiness and sense of well-being.

Self-Reflection

In what areas of your life would you like more calm, compassion, and clarity? What habitual reactionary patterns would you like to change?

Reviewing the past week (or month or year), what choices have you made that strengthen these qualities, and what choices have you made that weaken them?

What were the results? Internally and externally? Short-term and long-term?

Practice

Write the words "calm, compassion, clarity, choice" on a piece of paper and place it in various places around your home and work, taking time each day to reflect on what these words mean to you. Mentally preparing yourself for the next difficult encounter is essential for success.

Review previous difficult events and determine which of the four C's you used. Consider what you might haves done differently. Imagine bringing each quality to the situation. Review and preparation will help you to be more effective next time.

3

The Present Moment

"You must live in the present, launch yourself on every wave, find your eternity in each moment."
-Henry David Thoreau

(Mindfulness is bringing our awareness to the present moment. We observe what is arising now without grasping or rejecting. We practice the willingness to see with clarity while refraining from running storylines on what is arising in our experiences. We practice approaching our lives with a wise mind, an open heart and a gentle spirit. Mindful living is about waking up, becoming conscious, and living our lives fully.)

In truth, the present moment is all we have. Just this precious moment. This is it! Yet we often miss this moment, and the next, essentially losing the moments of our lives. We expend much of our mental and emotional energy either in the past or in the future. We regret the past. We review old conversations or experiences, especially those with an emotional charge. We run more storylines in our heads. We experience intense emotion, almost as if we are actually there. Interestingly, the brain can't distinguish between real and imagined. When we mentally review distressing events, we actually relive them. It's not as innocuous as it may seem. Our bodies respond by constricting with tension and by releasing cortisol, a stress hormone, into our blood stream.

We tend to stay overly busy. Internally, we worry, plan, or rehearse. Externally, we grasp for stimulation - internet, television, errands, food, drugs, people, and other distractions. Fear drives us to seek control and to avoid.

We spend much energy trying to control or avoid certain situations. Analysis-paralysis may result when we focus on what ifs, imagined conversations, or negative events. We often neglect what we actually **can** influence – our state of mind, our well-being, our responses to life. We then lose our personal power – our mental, emotional, and even physical energy.

Our lives are happening right now. We sometimes reject the present, imagining some other "perfect" moment. This is the perfect moment we've been waiting for. Even in its imperfection. ***This*** moment is occurring as it should. We reach for the next moment repeatedly, hoping for something better. We begin to feel ungrounded, overwhelmed, and scattered; unable to pay attention or be present.

We believe that busyness, an attempt to control, will make us safe. Mindfulness teaches us that such thinking is a type of illusion. We cannot control the outside world. We can, however, control our own responses to what life brings. We can shift from habitual reactionary patterns to conscious, skillful responding. In mindfulness, we can gain an internal sense of control and create a sense of safety that the outside world cannot take away.

Children and animals are excellent models of living in the present moment. If you watch a cat stretching in the sun or sitting peacefully on a windowsill, you see the embodiment of presence. Children immerse themselves completely in whatever they are doing. *Our nephew and godson, Jacob, loves to play with trucks and blocks. He also loves going to the playground and eating ice-cream.*

Whatever he does, he does with complete absorption. When we are with him, we are more awake and aware. Jacob reminds us regularly to inhabit the present moment.

Transcendentalist Henry David Thoreau, in Walden (1854), beautifully illustrates the experience of slowing down and enjoying the richness of each moment. He explains, "There were times when I could not afford to sacrifice the bloom of the present moment to any work, whether of the head or hand."How can you enjoy more Thoreau-esque moments?

Self-Reflection

In what ways are you missing the present moment? What are your patterns or tendencies?

Do you tend to get caught mentally in the past or the future?

What are you afraid of? What are you trying to control or avoid?

When do you feel most present and fully alive? How can you create more of these moments?

What are the consequences of not being present?

What benefits follow when being fully present?

Practice

To find moments of presence throughout your day, pause several times wherever you are, survey your surroundings while engaging all your senses (sight, smell, sound, touch, taste), take a deep full inhale, and release with a long slow exhale. Do this several times. Notice what the experience is like.

4

The Four Noble Truths

"These truths have a clear and simple message: It is the nature of life that all beings will face difficulties; through enlightened living one can transcend these difficulties, ultimately becoming fulfilled, liberated, and free."
–Lama Surya Das

Some people consider the message of the four noble truths to be negative or pessimistic. *When we (Angela and Dennis) read the first noble truth, that life is difficult, we nearly wept with relief and a sense of validation. So this is what is going on! For years we had interpreted our struggles as personal failings. This interpretation was difficult to accept when so much of what had occurred in our lives, beginning in childhood, seemed beyond our control.*

Yes, life is difficult. Life hands us pain that we do not want or choose – a cancer diagnosis, a parent's abandonment, a tornado destroying homes, the death of someone we love and need. And the list continues. Everyone experiences pain in some way. This is part of being human, a reality that no one can escape.

The second noble truth reminds us that we play a role in how much we suffer around life's pain. As humans, we add to our suffering through attachment, really wanting things to go our way. If we are too attached to an outcome, we add suffering to our pain. For example, some of our clients ask the question "Why me?" From a Buddhist psychology perspective, the answer is "Why not me?" Many of us have developed an expectation that life should progress in a linear fashion, from glory to glory. When events don't occur as we expect or prefer, we often react in ways that make the pain worse.

Marcus, a 25-year-old was so distraught about his parents' unexpected divorce that he did not speak to them for five years, despite the pleas of his father and other relatives. Marcus experienced extreme aversion (a form of attachment) to the reality of his parents' divorce. The ego in each of us manifests itself as resistance to what occurs in our lives. Resistance causes more dis-ease within us - mentally, emotionally, physically, and spiritually. Even if we don't prefer what is happening, we must first settle down in order to access clarity and equanimity. From this perspective, we can make wise decisions and take right action. In Marcus' case, his father became ill during the five years of separation. Fortunately, they were able to reconcile their relationship before his father's death.

Marcus came to understand that his parents had the right to live as they chose. Like Marcus, we can all get caught up in "what I want" and "what I expect." If we hold too tightly to these notions, we cause suffering to ourselves and others. Letting go is required. We learn to do this over and over, strengthening this muscle as we persevere.

The third noble truth brings good news. When we learn to respond skillfully to the world around us, we liberate ourselves from much unnecessary suffering. As we wake up, becoming more conscious in our lives and less driven by the ego, we have the opportunity for abiding peace. As we learn to untie the knots that bind us, that blind us to our true nature, we grow in our ability to live more fully and reside in equanimity, compassion, and joy. Mindfulness practice guides us in cultivating this skillfulness. Glimpses of this possibility develop into living this reality through practices such meditation, yoga, and studying the dharma.

The fourth noble truth reminds us that we can bring this open-hearted and grounded wisdom into everything we do. We take the experiences of awareness off the mat and into the world. Our lives become permeated with conscious living. We take a mindful approach in our conversations, our activities, our work, our relationships, our habits, and our choices. The Buddha offered instructions on how to do this through the Eight-fold Path. This path includes right view, right intentions, right speech, right action, right livelihood, right effort, right mindfulness, and right concentration. We invite you to answer the questions below to capture how you can apply this wisdom to your life.

Self-Reflection

Where have you seen these truths in your life?

How is your attachment, or "all caught up in me," causing you suffering?

Where can you choose to let go in your life?

Specific to the Eight-fold Path:

Right View – Are you willing to see things clearly, including yourself?

Right Intentions – What are the motivations beneath your actions? Are your motivations aligned with and congruent with your actions, or do you have another agenda? (Hint: Sometimes we have to dig deep here and practice radical honesty.)

Right Speech – Are you using conversation to help? Do you unconsciously participate in gossip or other harmful uses of words?

Right Action – Are your actions aligned with your deepest core values? Where are you putting your time, energy, and attention?

Right Livelihood – Is your career aligned with your deepest values? Does your job/organization help or cause harm? How are you using your money?

Right Effort – Can you find balance between holding on and letting go? Between doing and being? Are you able to practice the middle way? (Note: Some situations may take more practice.)

Right Mindfulness – Are you practicing being fully present in your life? How might you be missing the present moment? What are the consequences?

Right Concentration – In what areas are you able to bring your practice fully into what you are doing? Where is there separation? How do you need to achieve more integration?

Practice

When you are suffering – disappointed, uncomfortable, unsettled – examine the role your attachments play in that suffering. Think about how you might approach the situation differently to reduce your suffering.

5

Three Roots of Suffering

"The three poisons are always trapping you in one way or another, imprisoning you and making your world really small."
–Pema Chodron

Imagine someone sitting on the beach watching a beautiful sunset. Even though she is in a beautiful place, she may unconsciously react from one of the three roots of suffering. This person may respond by not only enjoying the sunset but by wishing she could witness more sunsets. She might continue her thinking by planning how she could get to the beach more often. She may continue by considering how she could make the next time even better – by bringing a soft blanket and pillows and some yummy snacks. Next, she may debate which snacks would be best to bring. In the meantime, the sun has set, and she was not fully present for it. This type of suffering is called grasping; always trying to improve the situation, wanting and reaching for more and better.

Another person may react by thinking that the air is too cool for the beach and that she should have worn something heavier for the weather. She may then go on mentally to have terse words with the weatherman who predicted a warm evening. She may continue by disparaging all weather forecasters, remembering the many plans that were ruined by inaccurate forecasts. In the meantime, the sun has set, and she was not fully present for it. This type of suffering is called aversion or aggression, resisting what is arising in life and focusing on what is wrong.

The third person may arrive on the beach just before sunset, often late for events she has planned for herself. Rather than catch the last moments, she may choose to stop at the vendor stand and purchase some snacks. By the time she gets settled on her blanket the sun has already set. This type of suffering is called delusion, ignorance, or denial, often presenting as a feeling of being scattered or confused.

Each tendency keeps us from experiencing the fullness of the present moment, the fullness of our lives. We can be caught by any one of these afflictions, but we generally have one that we lead with most often. The suffering that you lead with is considered your temperament type.

Each type has its downside and its upside. The good news is that, through mindfulness, we can heal and transform the negative qualities of our temperament. We must have the courage to acknowledge our actions through clear seeing and radical self-honesty. Compassion for ourselves as we investigate is essential. Using this information to berate ourselves is not skillful. We practice grounded, open-hearted clarity in mindfulness, especially as we turn the exploration toward ourselves. Our commitment to wake up to our dysfunctional patterns through insight and applied awareness directs us toward transforming these roots of suffering into inner strengths.

The person who has grasping tendencies can transform her suffering into qualities of positive acknowledgement, appreciation for the good in life, and process improvement. As she matures, she exudes warmth and supportiveness. The person who has aversive tendencies can spot problems quickly and become a part of the solution. Her development guides her to exude wisdom and an action orientation. The person who is deluded tends to be more flexible and easy-going once awake to her tendencies. She begins to exude equanimity and graciousness. As we transform these habitual tendencies into inner strengths, we shine our lights brightly, reducing suffering and helping ourselves and the world around us.

Self-Reflection

What is your lead temperament or type? What is your secondary type? Grasping, aversion, or delusion?

What type of feedback have you received from those around you that may help you identify your patterns?

Identify a few situations in which you have seen these patterns play out in your life.

Where have you seen progress in transforming these qualities into internal strengths? What is the positive side of your particular temperament?

Practice

Once you've determined your lead temperament type, notice its role as you move through the world. Consider the strengths of your type, and try consciously allowing that part of you to take the lead in your thoughts, conversation, and behaviors for the day.

6

Ego, Attachment, and Suffering

"Do you want peace or do you want pain?"
–*Eckhart Tolle*

While most of us respond to the opening quote with the answer "peace," much of what we do creates pain. Buddhist psychology suggests that the striving to attain happiness actually creates some of our suffering. We engage in many repetitive patterns that cause us more pain. We cannot change the pain that life delivers, but we can reduce our self-imposed suffering.

We are not our accomplishments, appearances, or acquisitions. The Western approach to life of "have more, be more, and do more" makes it difficult to be content with who we are and what we have in the present moment. We continue to grasp and strive for more, believing that "more" will make us happier. We have learned to build our happiness from the outside in, that when we get the right job, have more money, find the perfect mate, or achieve our perfect appearance, then we will be happy. Even when we have amazing experiences of achieving these things, soon we begin to worry about losing what we have achieved or acquired.

The ego encourages us to compare and compete in an attempt to build safety in the external world. When we compare ourselves to others, we objectify them and ourselves; this is unkind and blinds us to the beauty inherent in the uniqueness of each individual. The "better than" or "less than" position is a type of ego wounding. Internally, this process causes much suffering. Lao Tzu encourages us "to reside in our own sacred circle." If we allow ourselves to rest in our authentic selves, allowing ourselves to bloom just as we are, we retain our personal power.

In Practicing Peace in Times of War (2006), Pema Chodron discusses the choice between "spinning" or "holding our seat." The ego gets hooked in many ways – by wanting to be better, wanting to be special, wanting its way, etc. – and begins to spin. The hooking of the ego is called "shenpa." We may perceive others' shenpa clearly, but often miss our own. When our egos get hooked, we may start spinning - internally or externally, escalating in negative emotions, thought patterns, and behaviors. The instruction when we begin to spin is to "hold our seat."

With mindfulness, we practice noticing when the initial hook occurs. We feel a tightening in our bodies, minds, and hearts. At this point, we can choose to take a seat or spin out. When we choose to take a seat, we create a sacred pause, a time to breathe and relax into whatever arises in our experience. From here, we can access deeper wisdom. When we are angry or emotionally escalated, our cognitive abilities become blocked. We cannot think clearly. We make mistakes and cause pain, to ourselves and others. Holding our seat is a skillful approach to life's difficulties, and each time we choose this option, we strengthen this response within ourselves. Each time we indulge in spinning, we strengthen that reaction. We must ask ourselves, "Which response do I want to strengthen?"

Self-Reflection

What or who tends to hook you?

What does your spinning look like?

What are the results, internally and externally?

When have you been able to "hold your seat?" How did that feel?

Practice

When you know you are entering a situation that hooks you, prepare yourself.

Make a commitment that you will not spin out.

Breathe through the discomfort.

Congratulate yourself when you are successful, reinforcing effective habits.

7

Loving-Kindness

"The practice of lovingkindness is, in fact, the ground of mindfulness practice, requiring the same nonjudging, nongrasping, nonrejecting orientation toward the present moment, and orientation that invites and makes room for calmness, clarity of mind and heart, and understanding."
–Jon Kabat-Zinn

Leading with loving-kindness can be quite challenging in a world that often feels hostile, aggressive or uncaring. The stories on television in both the news and other programming highlight the dastardly deeds one perpetrates on another. As a culture, we seem drawn to this type of drama. Notice how you feel after watching one of these shows. You may feel tense and unsettled, maybe even angry and fearful. You may also notice when you watch comedies or positive programming, you feel more peaceful, happier, and settled. Mindful consumption of media helps us to practice loving-kindness in the world.

In a recent and extremely rare snowstorm in Atlanta, we were trapped in our homes for a week. We watched the news often to see when the dangerous conditions improved. We saw two stories of loving-kindness during the storm. First, a group of people with their children were stranded at a bus station. Buses were unable to run, and because of icy conditions, the group was unable to leave the station. A local restaurant heard about the situation, made their way to their restaurant, and provided meals for all these hungry people. In another story detailed, a woman was stranded at a local gas station. A couple saw her story on the news, got in their 4-wheel drive jeep, picked her up from the station and delivered her home safely. The loving-kindness of strangers is powerful and touching, reminding us of our inherent true nature - love.

In our Thursday morning mindfulness sangha at Cancer Wellness, we regularly discuss random acts of kindness. The group finds this uplifting and reinforcing. We shine a spotlight on the goodness in ourselves and those around us. The Buddha taught that it is skillful to take delight in one's own goodness, so we share how we have extended ourselves in random acts of kindness. We also discuss the ways in which we have received kindness as well as the kind acts we have witnessed.

This practice helps us focus on the good in the world and in ourselves. It is all too easy to overlook the good and focus on the bad. Research confirms the beneficial effects of kindness on the minds, bodies and spirits of all concerned. In The Power of Intention (2004), Dr. Wayne Dyer discusses the effect of kind acts on serotonin in the brain. He reviews a study in which the giver, receiver, and witness to an act of kindness all had an increase in this uplifting brain neurotransmitter.

Metta is the Sanskrit word for loving-kindness. Loving-kindness is taught as the first of four brahma-viharas, cornerstones of the Buddha's teachings. They are often called the divine abodes, the best places to live. The other brahma-viharas are compassion, joy, and equanimity; each are discussed in other chapters.

Our egos lead us to block metta through judgment, ambition, greed, insecurity and the need to control. When we indulge in these unskillful habits, we water the seeds of negativity within us. Loving-kindness is a training. When we bring the qualities of mindfulness -loving-kindness, compassion, joy and equanimity – to a situation, we water the positive seeds in ourselves. The more we practice, the better able we are to make conscious choices about our thoughts, words, and behaviors. We become the powerful, loving people we truly are. We are each a force for good in this world when we access and act from our true nature.

> *The thought manifests as the word;*
> *The word manifests as the deed;*
> *The deed develops into habit;*
> *And habit hardens into character.*
> *So watch the thought and its ways with care,*
> *And let it spring from love*
> *Born out of concern for all beings.*
>
> *-The Buddha*

Simply refraining from blaming, judging, and thinking harshly of others does not mean that we deny their difficult qualities. Our wisdom and clear seeing allow us to see others in all their humanity. We retain and even enhance our ability for discernment. Loving-kindness does not mean that we choose to have a deep and intimate relationship with everyone. It's healthy and appropriate to vary the types of relationships in which we choose to engage. We may have some people with whom we connect on a regular basis and others with whom we speak less often. There are even some that we may see only once or twice a year. Discerning which relationships are right for us is a part of creating balance and health in our lives.

There are some people who are not a good fit for us in relationship. As the wise teacher Sylvia Boorstein reminds us in Happiness is an Inside Job: Practicing for a Joyful Life (2007), "You can put people out of your life but not out of your heart." Sometimes you have to put people out of your life in order to keep them in your heart. There are people in our lives whom we may love dearly but cannot afford to connect with very often because of their impact on us.

As counselors we often see clients choosing to keep people in their lives while building resentment or even contempt towards them. This is not helpful for anyone. Some of our clients have so much toxic energy in their lives, they have to "clean house" with friends, family, and even business associates. This realization is even more important when a client is trying to get sober.

Jerry is a highly successful attorney who came to us because his professional license was threatened due to a second DUI charge. Jerry's lifestyle was "living large." He was attached to his identity as "big man on campus." He wined and dined everyone - friends, family, and business associates. He worked hard, and he partied hard.

At first, he was able to maintain the long hours at work while partying at night. At 45, he was feeling the effects of progressive alcoholism. His mind wasn't as sharp. His weight and blood pressure had risen substantially. He was drinking more and more each year, and he wasn't having as much fun. Getting sober for Jerry meant changing his lifestyle, some of which meant letting go of certain friends, family, and business associates.

For some time after Jerry became sober, he tried hard to retain the same playmates and playgrounds. Yet he found his resentment growing when his companions drank excessively and encouraged him to drink as well. His breaking point came when his brothers took him to a sports bar. After extensive drinking, his youngest brother wanted to drive home. Through sobriety, Jerry could see much more clearly how dangerous and selfish this was. His brother could barely walk. Jerry got into a fight with his other brothers over this dilemma. The situation was resolved when the youngest brother passed out, and Jerry took him home.

Finally, Jerry realized he had to loosen his attachment to his previous identity and way of relating and "clean house," understanding his own limits and setting firm boundaries with everyone in his life. Although he went through a period of unease and ambiguity, Jerry now feels that he is living a healthy, happy and truly successful life. The DUI charge, which looked to be a misfortune, soon became a blessing.

Taking care of ourselves is essential to our well-being. In metta meditation, we start with ourselves, rejoicing in our own internal goodness and light. Some meditation practitioners retreat for long periods, focusing solely on metta for self. For many of us, it is complex to open our hearts to ourselves, with unconditional love and acceptance. The ego is always ringing the bell of "not enough." We discover numerous ways to judge and reject ourselves. We truly break our own hearts when we relate to ourselves from a place of intermittent or perpetual negativity. When we focus on our goodness, we build positive self-esteem and self-regard.

Bapuji, an Indian master in the Vedantic tradition, captures the beauty of loving-kindness for the self in the following poem:

> *My beloved child*
>
> *Break your heart no longer.*
>
> *Each time you judge yourself*
>
> *you break your own heart.*
>
> *You stop feeding on the love which is the wellspring of your vitality.*
>
> *The time has come, your time*
>
> *to live,*
>
> *to celebrate*
>
> *and to see the goodness that you are…*
>
> *Let no one, no thing, no idea or ideal obstruct you*
> *If one comes, even in the name of "Truth,"*
>
> *forgive it for its Unknowing.*
>
> *Do not fight.*
>
> *Let go.*
>
> *And breathe---into the goodness that you are.*

Each person on this planet is unique and irreplaceable, an exquisite miracle to behold. There will never be a replica of anyone. The Buddha taught that true enlightenment would be falling in love with everyone all day long. We could see into their true nature, and we would not be blocked by the ego. The light between us would be immensely pleasurable because all parties would be immersed in deep and penetrating true love.

If you've ever attended a retreat or an extended workshop, you may have experienced the deep wellspring within your own heart, overflowing in love for those around you. Whenever we practice metta meditation in a group, the energy in the room shifts palpably. Upon closing, many participants inevitably exclaim "I want to do this more! I feel so good!" Metta practice is a powerful elixir, shifting us into a more joyful, heart-expanded, connected, and peaceful state. It lifts us out of our isolating self-centeredness and delivers us to a place of well-being.

When we are happy with ourselves, we extend ourselves honestly in loving-kindness to others. When we feel peaceful and filled with love and joy, we assess others more generously. We give them the benefit of the doubt, extending mercy and patience. We look skillfully at the context of situations rather than solely focusing on a behavior or event we do not prefer. Our perspectives become wiser and guided with equanimity.

When we extend ourselves to others in loving-kindness, we heal something in them and in ourselves. The energy of metta is a balm that reminds us that we are all worthy of loving-kindness. When people feel seen and cared for, it ignites the goodness within them. A ripple effect of kindness begins to emerge. We are each such a powerful force for good when we water wholesome seeds within our hearts and minds.

We had the good fortune of retreating with Sharon Salzberg for a weekend at Atlanta's Drepung Loseling Monastery. She has an immense and depthful understanding of metta practice, both formally and informally. She has been practicing and teaching for many years, and we find that just being in her presence brings a sense of warmth, safety, and acceptance. Our response to her demonstrates the energy each of us brings into the world, depending on our focus and choices. If you respond positively to something in your teacher, you have that very same quality within you. This is why it resonates. In one exercise during the retreat, Sharon guided us to walk mindfully through a park, offering metta to ourselves. Every participant reported how nourished they felt (mentally, emotionally, physically, and spiritually) at the end of this very simple but powerful exercise, extending the tenderness and love to themselves that they often reserve for others.

Self-Reflection

List your qualities rooted in goodness.

How do you show loving-kindness to yourself? To others?

List specifics.

What blocks loving-kindness in your life? (fear, judgment, anger, negative self-talk, lack of self-care, unforgiveness)

Practice

Metta Meditation

Loving-kindness does not always arise organically. We must train in developing and strengthening this quality within ourselves. Try the meditation below.

First, pick one person for each category and then write the name beside each:

Self

Benefactor (someone who has helped you in a small or big way)

Loved One (someone with whom you have no negative emotional charge today, someone who evokes big and easy love in your heart)

Neutral Person (someone you don't know, a stranger, perhaps someone you passed today or yesterday, no emotional charge)

Difficult Person (someone with whom you have had difficulties - start with a less difficult person, gradually progressing to more difficult people as you become more adept at this meditation).

All Living Beings

Once you have identified one person for each category, stick with that person. You can use a different person next time. This also helps to build concentration.

Find a comfortable place and move into your meditation posture. Close your eyes and find your breath, allowing your breath to settle you down and settle you in for meditation. With each out-breath, feel yourself letting go more and more of the outside world, bringing your awareness within. Bring your awareness to your heart, recognizing your own inherent goodness. Feel the tenderness, the soft spot that resides there. As your awareness rests there, feel the energy of loving-kindness begin to expand, becoming even stronger and more present.

Bring yourself to mind, seeing yourself in all your humanity, recognizing the precious gift that you are. Open your heart, sending love and acceptance to yourself. You may even want to say your name to yourself. Try using a term of endearment "My precious (your name). Now offer the phrases of metta to yourself….

May I be filled with loving-kindness.

May I be held in loving-kindness.

May I be free from suffering.

May I know great joy and deep and abiding peace.

May I awaken and be free.

Breathing in and breathing out.

Now bring to mind your benefactor, seeing this person as clearly as possible, imagining where s/he might be at this moment. Knowing that when s/he helped you, s/he was in a place of strength. Knowing that they too experience vulnerability, insecurity, and restlessness at times. Now offer the phrases of metta to your benefactor, starting with his/her name.

May you be filled with loving-kindness...etc.

Now bring to mind your loved one, seeing this person as clearly as possible, imagining where s/he might be at this moment. Notice the energy of loving-kindness expand as you focus on this person. Now, offer the phrases of metta to your loved one.

Breathing in and breathing out.

Now bring to mind a neutral person, someone you do not know. Perhaps you've crossed paths with this person in the last day or so. It could be a person in the next car, the grocery store clerk, or someone you noticed in a parking lot. It's important that you not have a negative or positive emotional charge when thinking of this person. Although you do not know this person, s/he has known 10,000 joys and 10,000 sorrows as you and your loved ones have. This person wishes to be happy and peaceful, just as you and your loved ones do. Imagine where s/he might be in this moment as you offer phrases of metta to him or her.

Breathing in and breathing out.

Now bring to mind a difficult person. If you are new at this practice, perhaps try someone you like or love but are struggling with at this moment. Once you have practiced for some time, you can begin to use the more difficult people in your life, those who behave in ways that are off-putting, those who may have hurt you in some way. If you notice resistance or negative emotions like anger or fear, hold these, too, in the energy of loving-kindness. Continue to hold yourself in loving-kindness. This part of metta brings to mind the quote by Henry Longfellow Wadsworth: "If we knew the secret history of our enemies, it would disarm all hostility." We see the behavior that we do not prefer in another but mindfulness reminds us of the context in which that behavior arose; the context we do not know about. And sometimes, those who are most difficult are those who need it the most. In A Christmas Carol (1843), Mr. Scrooge's nephew Fred is a great example of pure love for his uncle, even though Mr. Scrooge is quite difficult to love. Despite Scrooge's insolence, Fred never gives up in sending him kind wishes. Perhaps Fred focused on his uncle's inner goodness. Now offer the phrases of metta to the difficult person you have identified.

Breathing in and breathing out.

Now bring to mind all living beings. This includes all humans, animals, even the grasshoppers and ants. You may find it helpful to begin with those in your near circumference, then your city, then your state, continuing to broaden your energy to include all living beings everywhere. Now offer the phrases of metta to all.

Breathing in and breathing out.

Take a moment to bathe in the warmth and generosity of your metta practice, recognizing that this is your true nature. Take in a few deep inhales and release with long slow exhales. Now you may begin to wiggle your fingers and toes as a way to start coming back into the room, adjusting your head and body in any way you wish and gently opening your eyes with soft eyes, coming back into the room slowly.

In this meditation, we used the traditional phrases of metta. You may use any phrases that resonate with you. Here are a few examples:

May you be well.

May you be happy.

May you be at peace.

May you be safe.

May you live with ease.

We guided you through formal metta meditation, but you can also practice informally. You may choose to offer silently phrases of metta to people with whom you cross paths each day. We enjoy offering metta at stores or while waiting in lines. We notice a shift in our perspective and energy.

Again, if you encountered any resistance when offering metta to yourself, practice only on yourself for a period until you feel the energy of loving-kindness penetrating, and you open your heart to yourself with unconditional love and acceptance. Then you can practice for others.

If you found it challenging to offer metta to your difficult person, you may want to continue focusing on that person until you feel more peaceful when you bring this person to mind. Remember that offering metta is not a concession or an agreement with his/her behavior. This practice releases us from our internal knots of suffering.

We (Angela and Dennis) offered metta to one person for months before we were able to shift. Interestingly, when we saw this person again, we had almost no emotional charge with him. What a feeling of freedom! We liberated ourselves from the chains of suffering, and you can, too.

Some people struggle when offering metta to all living beings. One of our teachers, Larry Ward, co-founder of the Lotus Institute, enjoys using the sensation and image of love moving from his heart out to others as a way to practice metta. He imagines his energy moving through the building he is in, touching everyone present, then moving down the streets of the city, across the state, and eventually around the world. You may want to try this approach also.

8

Compassion

"Compassion is first the 'clear seeing' of pain and second, the opening to it, establishing an appropriate relationship to it, not being overwhelmed or debilitated by it."
–Sharon Salzberg

In our culture, when we hear the word compassion, we often think of softness and warmth. Some even associate it with passivity and weakness. In mindfulness, compassion is considered a great strength, backed by wisdom and equanimity. Compassion is not about allowing our boundaries to be violated or silencing our voices. We do not become doormats or give ourselves away. We think and act from a place of clarity and open-heartedness. In compassion, we respond skillfully to ourselves and others.

There is clear evidence that living from a place of compassion is excellent for health. Compassion meditation, for example, reduces inflammation and cortisol levels in the body. Over time, the brain is altered positively, yielding a happier disposition. Based on a 2008 Emory study, "Effect of Compassion Meditation on Neuroendocrine, Innate Immune and Behavioral Responses to Psychosocial Stress," Charles Raison, M.D., concluded, "Our findings suggest that meditation practices designed to foster compassion may impact physiological pathways that are modulated by stress and are relevant to disease." This research illustrates that we can intervene in the process of disease formation by practicing compassion meditation. Realizing the power we have to positively influence our health is the first step towards wellness.

In Oriah Mountain Dreamer's poem (and book by the same name – see references section for more information), The Invitation, (1999), one stanza reads:

> *"I want to know*
> *if you can sit with pain*
> *mine or your own*
> *without moving to hide it*
> *or fade it*
> *or fix it."*

When we read this poem aloud at workshops, we inevitably get a strong reaction from the audience. Being seen is one of the greatest human longings. In our work as counselors and coaches, we are thanked most for listening. Bearing witness to another's suffering, without judging it or shrinking back, heals. Oriah offers great wisdom about the power of facing pain, ours and others.

Our friend, poet, and certified poetry therapist, John Fox, author of Finding What You Didn't Lose: Expressing Your Truth and Creativity through Poem-Making (1995), works extensively in the integrative medicine arena. He speaks to the value of listening in this beautifully-expressed poem:

> *"When Someone Deeply Listens To You"*
>
> *When someone deeply listens to you*
> *it is like holding out a dented cup*
> *you've had since childhood*
> *and watching it fill up with*
> *cold, fresh water.*
> *When it balances on top of the brim,*
> *you are understood.*
> *When it overflows and touches your skin,*
> *you are loved.*

When someone deeply listens to you
the room where you stay
starts a new life
and the place where you wrote
your first poem
begins to glow in your mind's eye.
It is as if gold has been discovered!

When someone deeply listens to you
your barefeet are on the earth
and a beloved land that seemed distant
is now at home within you.

Many of our clients have endured horrific physical and sexual abuse. Amanda was molested by her mother's boyfriend beginning at age seven. Kevin and his sister were both physically abused by their father throughout their childhood. Christina was left to fend for herself beginning at the age of five, often going without food or proper clothing.

We (Angela and Dennis) hear many horror stories…and we work with our clients through many types of intervention. We use anxiety reduction strategies, meditation, yoga, and visualization. We also use facilitated writing and empty chair techniques so that our clients can find and honor their voices, the voices they could not use as children. We work deeply and arduously to help. And yet, what we hear the most from them are words of gratitude for seeing and hearing them, for witnessing their suffering without moving away, for listening deeply.

Some move away from suffering in both obvious ways and more subtle ways. Some people simply refuse to acknowledge the reality of suffering. Some minimize what is occurring while others maximize it. Some simply change the subject. Some intellectualize it. Some focus on themselves, unable to focus on another's suffering. Some become extremely emotional so **they** are the ones who need the comforting. Some give pat answers or offer quick fixes. Some philosophize or offer empty spiritual adages. If you've ever been on the receiving end, you know how bad these approaches can feel.

Stories are often told at Cancer Wellness about well-meaning friends and family members distancing themselves in the above ways once someone has been diagnosed with cancer. These maneuvers are what we call "unskillful" in mindfulness. Often, we reach out to other wounded birds who are simply unable to be present for us during difficult times. It can be surprising who shows up in terms of support during times of trouble and who does not. Some people are not skillful in exhibiting compassion. This experience reminds us of the suffering inherent in expectations; that sometimes **we** need to release our attachment to people responding in a certain way.

For some people, compassion arises organically. Compassion is also learned through training. Compassion is taught as the second brahma-vihara; the other three include loving-kindness, joy, and equanimity. The brahma-viharas are the cornerstones of Buddhist teachings. The mantra "Om Mani Padme Hum" reminds us that when we meditate, creating spaciousness in ourselves and our lives, compassion and wisdom naturally arise. Similarly, we must train in compassion to be consistent in responding skillfully to suffering. We set the intention to be compassionate people, and we work towards keeping our hearts open and our feet grounded when witnessing suffering.

Understanding boundaries as part of compassion is essential as we integrate this powerful practice into our daily lives. While we train in compassion, we realize we are each human, and we all have limits. *Even as counselors and meditation teachers, we reach our limits and take time to relax and unwind. Usually at night, we (Angela and Dennis) take a break from listening. We turn off the phone and the computer. If we choose to watch a movie, we select one that is lighter, less heart-impacting.*

In the helping profession, "compassion fatigue" is a term often used. Doctors, nurses, counselors, and other helpers have limits, and if they overextend, they find themselves less able to be present and compassionate with those they are trying to help. Lay persons as well can succumb to compassion fatigue. Compassion fatigue, though it implies that a person is merely tired, is actually considered to be a form of trauma. In helping a loved one, we may become vulnerable to this syndrome. Everyone needs breaks - physically, emotionally, and mentally. It is imperative to recharge and practice self-care. If you are in a caregiving role, it is very easy to put yourself on the back burner for too long. With compassion, we must all find our own innate balance.

Todd had been struggling with the fallout from HIV for years. His energy was reduced. He often felt nauseated. He worried about his finances due to medication expenses and inadequate insurance coverage.

Rather than asking for help, Todd kept going about his life as if his problems did not exist. Every day, he would see clients, help take care of his aging mother, and listen to his friends' woes patiently. He denied and minimized the pain he was in, even when his friends offered to help. Eventually, Todd reached his breaking point. He finally opened his heart to himself, allowed himself to cry, and sought help from those willing to support and bolster him. It takes courage to be compassionate, with ourselves and others, to face pain with clarity and open-heartedness.

In ancient teachings, "idiot compassion" is discussed. We prefer to call it "mindless compassion." Remembering that compassion is guided by wisdom, it's important for us to discern whether our compassionate decisions are grounded. Codependency and enabling actions are forms of "mindless compassion." If a loved one has a pattern of quitting jobs repeatedly when they become bored or impatient, it is unskillful and mindless to pay their bills. If your adult child will not get a job, it is mindless compassion that guides you to house him. If your brother struggles with drug addiction, it is unskillful to make excuses for him. These examples of codependency actually harm you and the other person. Releasing others to live their lives as they choose, without trying to control the outcome is practicing compassion, wisdom, and equanimity.

We can become blocked in our compassion training in many ways. Fear and anger cloud compassion. Sometimes, we aren't even aware that we are scared or angry. We may have stuffed, denied, or distorted our feelings in some way. These feelings may be whispered emotions that require deep listening to decipher. Self-awareness is key. The ego is an obstacle. We may expect reciprocity or acknowledgement. Our desires to control, manipulate, or demand an outcome become blocks to true compassion. If you extend yourself to someone, and find yourself with expectation or resentment, this could be a red flag for further investigation.

Compassionate acts can be big or small. They can be tangible or intangible. You may choose to stop by the grocery store for someone, or send them well-wishes during your meditation. You may choose to assess someone and their actions more generously, less harshly. You may choose to take a mental health day or do some journal writing. You may say something kind to yourself each morning upon waking. There are many ways to practice.

Recent, compelling research points to the significance of the vagus nerve, "the nerve of compassion," the body's caretaking organ. Dr. Dascher Keltner of UC-Berkeley highlights groundbreaking scientific research about the roots of compassion and altruism. Dr. Keltner concurs with the work of physiological psychologist Dr. Steve Borges. According to Dr. Borges, when observing acts of compassion or meditating on compassion, we experience a calming effect in our hearts via the vagus nerve bundle. This seems to occur in various ways, particularly through the stimulation of oxytocin receptors, strong neuropeptides intimately involved in the emotions of trust and love. Practicing compassion directly affects the heart; the heart of the giver, receiver and observer.

When compassion is practiced in meditation and in the world, and the amygdala is altered in such a way that we can withstand more intense emotion, both others' and our own, we rebound to a calm state more quickly. Much research supports this, including that of Daniel Goleman and Tara Bennett-Goleman (2001). They assert that meditation is effective due to the relationship between the amygdala and the prefrontal cortex. Through practice, we are less likely to make snap judgments and are able to tolerate the intense emotions of others and ourselves.

As a gift to Angela on her birthday, Dennis bought a beautiful statue of Kuan Yin, the goddess of compassion, sitting on top of the heart sutra. The image is graceful, powerful, and compassionate. We keep it in our foyer as a reminder of the centrality of compassion in our lives and in our practice. You may find it helpful to keep a visual symbol of compassion in your environment also.

Self-Reflection

What memories do you have of someone extending themselves to you or of you extending to others in compassion?

How do you relate to pain, yours or others? Are you able to bear witness to suffering without being overwhelmed by it – either debilitated or distanced?

How are you practicing compassion for yourself now? What would you like to add?

Practice

Write a love letter to yourself, with only affirmative, compassionate statements. Then read it aloud to yourself several times a week.

Notice the internal shifts that begin occur.

If you are truly brave, read it aloud to yourself in the mirror.

9

Joy

"Breathing in, I smile."
-Thich Nhat Hanh

Being joyful feels incredibly good to the self, on all levels. When we smile, the muscles in our face relax and we feel better, and yet, we allow countless people, events and obstacles to block our joy. When we discuss joy with meditation and yoga students, most report they want more of it in their lives. Many find that a dharma talk on this subject reminds them of something they've forgotten to include consciously in their lives.

Joy is one of the four brahma-viharas in mindfulness teachings. The other three include loving-kindness, compassion, and equanimity. The Sanskrit name for joy is *mudita*. Brahma-viharas are considered the cornerstones of the teachings and are often called "the four divine abodes," the best places to live. The Buddha taught that cultivating joy in our lives is skillful. There are many ways to cultivate it, starting today.

Gratitude is an ally of joy. When we pause to remember the many blessings in our lives, we become more joyful. We sometimes forget gratitude for the simple things, like being able to see or hear. Susan attended a yoga and meditation retreat we facilitated. She reported having trouble with her eyes the previous year. For six months, she suffered until one doctor was able to treat her condition. Luckily, her eyesight returned to normal, and she told us there is not a day that passes when she isn't grateful for her eyesight. And yet, most of us don't consider how fortunate we are to see, hear, breathe, or walk.

Researchers have found that gratitude practice affects the receptor sites in the brain, strengthening our immune system. Dr. Robert Emmons, a psychology professor at the University of California at Davis and a leading authority on gratitude, recognizes the benefits of gratitude in Thanks!: How the New Science of Gratitude Can Make You Happier (2007). In addition to structural alterations to the brain itself, Dr. Emmons demonstrates how gratitude contributes to emotional equanimity and pleasure, richer personal relationships, and improved health. We recommend keeping a gratitude journal. Each morning upon waking or each night before sleeping, take a few moments to recognize the many blessings in your life. This practice will expand your heart, allowing for more joy.

His Holiness the Dalai Lama tells us that when we take joy in others' good fortune, **our** opportunities for joy increase six billion to one. Who wouldn't want those odds? One translation of "mudita" is sympathetic joy; rejoicing in the happiness of others. Imagine feeling the same excitement for others that you feel for yourself and your loved ones. Good fortune is occurring all around us. Rather than remaining neutral or mildly excited, try feeling joy for others as you do when you have good news.

For Angela, it is truly a pleasure spending time with Dennis. He finds joy in so many things. His heart is wide open. He easily recognizes and acknowledges tenderness and humanity in another. When receiving a gift, even a small one, his enthusiasm lights up the room and warms Angela's heart. He is one of the most excited and gracious receivers. He laughs often and finds humor in even the not-so-funny situations. He makes the people around him smile and laugh. His joy is contagious. The people around us help to cultivate joy or block it. Likewise, the events in which we participate, the television or music we consume, and the daily choices we make, all affect our levels of joy.

When we take the time to become mindful of the world we live in – **really** seeing the grass, the trees, the people - our hearts fill with joy. When we take time to witness the miraculous beauty of the world, we are awe-struck and joy-full. The wonder and mystery of the world, the natural elements, and the precious people inhabiting it, are always available to us. This way of truly seeing life around us is depicted in the movie Avatar (2009) when one character reaches for the other, and says "I see you." When we look at one another with fresh eyes, putting aside all of our projections and mental models, everyone involved experiences a moment of grace.

Our ego's need to be right, to judge others, and to be important blocks our full potential for joy. The negative stories we tell ourselves produce fear, insecurity, envy, and a sense of lack. Our egos tell us that there is not enough for us all, so we must win at all costs; that we are not enough, so we must continue to strive, even at the cost of our health and relationships. Our ego-driven thoughts tell us to distance and withhold or to compare and compete. The ego energizes itself through fear and judgment. Conquer and divide is its mantra.

Our deeper identity, the witness within, knows that the ego distorts the truth. When we increase our access to this deeper identity through meditation and contemplation, we can release fear-based ways of thinking and acting.

A lack of joy can impede our good health. In You Can Beat the Odds: The Surprising Factors Behind Chronic Illness and Cancer (2009), Brenda Stockdale reviews provocative research studies in the Journal of Occupational and Environmental Medicine, the Journal of the American Medical Association, Neurology, and Epidemiology. This research explains that depression is the single best predictor of cardiovascular disease, not the traditional indicators of history, smoking, diabetes, high blood pressure, or high cholesterol. Joy is essential to our well-being.

We had the good fortune of participating in a workshop with Dr. Dan Siegel, a prominent researcher in the field of integrative medicine, specifically in the neurobiology of mindfulness. In Mindfulness and the Brain (2010), he discusses meditation's ability to changes our set point for happiness. Meditation improves our experience of joy. This type of joy is called eudemonia, a state in which the practitioner feels a sense of equanimity, balance, connection, and well-being.

As human beings, we have a tendency to place emphasis on what is wrong - with us, with others, and with the world. However, heaven and hell are constantly co-arising. *Even as Angela's father was losing his battle to lung cancer, we would connect with him nightly by phone, and he would ask, "What beach do you want to meet at in our dreams tonight?" We would discuss all the possibilities, and this ritual would bring a smile to our hearts. Even though we were all very sad about his declining condition, we chose to shine the spotlight on our shared joy.*

With mindfulness practice, we learn to hold both at the same time, to enjoy heaven even though hell is present. Hell does not trump heaven, but sometimes we allow it to. In reality, if we allow heaven's joy into our hearts, we become more resilient and capable of navigating hell. Through mindfulness practice, we also learn to focus on what is right - with us, with others, and with the world.

Similarly, the Lebanese mystic Khalil Gibran wrote this of joy in The Prophet (1923): "Verily you are suspended like scales between your sorrow and your joy. Only when you are empty are you at standstill and balanced." Mindfulness is a practice of emptying, allowing joy and sorrow to flow through us and be released.

Self-Reflection

Who and what brings you joy? How much time do you spend with those who bring you joy?

What blocks your joy (ego, judgment, insecurity, need to be right or important, greed, ambition, people, thoughts)?

How would you like to cultivate more joy in your life?

Practice

Each day, commit to one thing that brings you more joy. It may be connecting with a friend who loves and accepts you unconditionally. It may be an activity you enjoy. Perhaps you choose to invest in humor or engage in more laughter, a different way of thinking or behaving, letting go of something. Try to incorporate something different, something you have not tried before.

Start a gratitude journal. Remember the large blessings and the small ones.

10

Equanimity

"True peace is not indifference or emotional resignation;
it is the still point, the living reality of the present."
–Jack Kornfield

Two Buddhist monks were walking along a path when they came to a shallow, muddy river. A woman in a beautiful dress waited there, not wishing to cross for fear of ruining her dress. One of the monks lifted her onto his shoulders – something that he was absolutely **not** *supposed to do – and carried her to the other side, where he set her down and proceeded along the path with his fellow monk. After a few hours, the second monk, unable to keep quiet about what he understood as a violation of the code by which they lived, asked his companion, "Why did you pick that woman up and carry her across the river?" The first monk replied, "Are you still carrying her? I put her down hours ago."*

Letting go is key to experiencing equanimity in life. And yet, we resist letting go at every turn. Equanimity, called "upekka" in Sanskrit, can be characterized in several ways. It can be described as deep and abiding peace, a radiant calm, or stillness and poise. Equanimity is the calm in the storm. It is taught as the fourth brahma-vihara because it grounds and balances the other three heart-expanding brahma-viharas of loving-kindness, compassion, and joy.

We say that we want deep and abiding peace, and yet, when we realize that we must let go of a few things to experience peace, we, like the monk in the above vignette, continue to hold on tightly. We want control, and we think we are losing ground when we let go. And yet, control is an illusion. We do and say many "insane" things in an attempt to control. The 12-step adage describes it well: "The definition of insanity is doing the same things over and over and expecting different results." We laugh knowingly when we hear this because we see ourselves in it.

In the Buddha's teachings on the eight worldly winds, we are reminded that the world is constantly changing. Change and letting go are kissing cousins. When we master letting go, we master the skillful navigation of change. The eight worldly winds include pleasure and pain, gain and loss, praise and blame, and fame and disrepute. These consistently arise and pass away, largely out of our control. The winds of change can blow us around like a leaf. When practicing equanimity, we feel the wind but remain grounded and centered in the midst of it.

One of us may do a beautiful cartwheel in the middle of the room and everyone cheers for us, praising us for our cartwheel adeptness. The next week, we may do the same cartwheel, for the very same audience, and they may find fault with the technicalities of the cartwheel or that we even chose to do a cartwheel at all. Praise and blame constantly arise and pass away, and often have nothing to do with us. And yet, we personalize them, clinging tightly to praise and spiraling downward when we are blamed. Equanimity guides us to release our attachment to both, as we understand the wisdom of impermanence. In her CD/audiotape Getting Unstuck (2006), Pema Chodron shares with listeners that since the huge success of her published teachings, she has never been so praised in her life. Nor has she ever been so blamed. This phenomenon is universal.

Working with cancer patients, survivors, and their loved ones at Cancer Wellness at Piedmont Hospital, we watch these brave men and women work through the worldly winds of gain and loss. Being diagnosed with cancer is traumatic. The loss of health is one of the greatest losses a person can experience in life. And yet, we are struck and touched by their bravery as participants work through this loss and find their way back to a place of peace. Sometimes the peace is only glimpsed at first. As they continue to focus their intention on wellness, participating in the various healing programs Cancer Wellness offers, the equanimity in them becomes stronger and more abiding, and soon they are reaching out to others in the community. Not only do we see these amazing men and women reach out to the cancer community, they often become lights of healing for their friends and families.

Ron, a cancer survivor in our sangha, rode bikes competitively for many years before diagnosis. After diagnosis and treatment, he could no longer ride as he did before. He could barely circle his neighborhood block without getting winded. Initially, he suffered greatly over this loss. Riding bikes had given him considerable pleasure and stress relief over the years. One day, in our weekly sangha, Ron told the group about a realization - that he was not a bike rider, but a man who enjoyed riding bikes. This was an epiphany for him. Ron began to notice other things as well. As he climbed Stone Mountain, he began cheering silently for other climbers when previously he would have become competitive, focusing on getting to the top first. He even made connections with other hikers. Ron reported feeling much more joy, compassion, and equanimity within.

Ron, as well as others, chose to let go of life before cancer ("bc," they often call it), and he has reaped the benefits. He would tell you that he is living a rich and happy life. Watching the courageous transformation of so many of our Cancer Wellness participants is humbling and inspiring.

As we practice equanimity, we create a spaciousness within and around us. This spaciousness, called "shunyata" in Sanskrit, occurs when we choose to let go. There is so much we can choose to release, from the remarks of a co-worker to the old loves who broke our hearts. We can let go of our busyness, our need to be right, our need to get our way, our need for others to see it our way, our constant striving and grasping. We start with the more innocuous "letting go's" and build up to the more difficult and complex "letting go's. "

As we release our striving to be more, have more, and do more, we relax the mind, heart, body, and spirit.. We are led to a freshness, an openness, and an abiding peace within. When we strive constantly, reaching for the next thing, reaching for more, we constrict. Constriction of the mind, heart, and body does not lead to wellness. It actually causes pain. As you become more mindful, you become more acutely aware of the pain that results from excessively reaching, strivng, extending, and doing. Constriction also causes the release of cortisol, a stress hormone secreted by the adrenal glands and directly linked to various diseases. Researchers Judith A. Whitworth, et al. in "Cushing, Cortisol, and Cardiovascular Disease," (2000) discuss the role of cortisol as a contributing factor in disease formation. Staying too busy, internally or externally, is counterproductive, to our health and well-being.

We all have our favorite ways of filling each and every moment. *Angela is a book junkie, and Dennis loves to surf the internet.* While there is nothing wrong with surfing the net or reading, any activity can be overdone. When we are unable to center ourselves in the present, we cannot find the radiant calm we seek. We may fill our moments with running errands, doing chores, making lists, watching television, talking to others, checking emails and texts, eating or working. Likewise, staying too busy internally, through worrying, planning, focusing too much on the past or the future, also creates pain and constriction in the mind, heart, body.

Pema Chodron calls this the "all-caught-up-ness" that blocks our shunyata and our equanimity. If we settle down into the present moment more often during each day, we will find that we are more peaceful, wise, productive, and loving beings. We can do this by inserting sacred pauses into our day. Sacred pauses can be incorporated by stopping whatever you are doing, taking a few breaths, elongating each outbreath to connect you with the spaciousness that is already within and around you, centering yourself. The exhalation is a literal and figurative process of letting go. You may choose to do some mindful yoga or some chanting, perhaps a prayer, before you drop into the stillness and the spaciousness within.

Starting your day with meditation creates a day of equanimity and shunyata. *On most days, we (Angela and Dennis) practice our meditation and yoga upon waking. On other days, we eat breakfast, work out, and then practice. Sometimes, we can even add a second practice session towards the end of the day.* Practicing first thing in the morning is recommended, even if sitting for only five minutes each day. Beginning the day in quiet alters the quality of the day. Mystics reportedly meditated for an hour in the morning and an hour in the evening, and some even more. That's a tall order for most of us. When we find the time to add an afternoon or evening meditation, we integrate the day's events and enjoy a better night's sleep. Sleeping, of course, is a big letting go. If you have trouble sleeping, it may be a sign of holding on too tightly.

Equanimity also requires wisdom, compassion (for ourselves and others), and acceptance. We must be able to discern clearly what is occurring. It's important that we keep our hearts open to ourselves and others, even if we disagree with what is occurring. Some students on this path mistake indifference for equanimity. Distancing or relating only from a cerebral perspective is not equanimity. Teachers call it equanimity "with an edge." It may look like equanimity to some extent, but the quality beneath the thoughts, words, or actions results from a subtle shutting of the heart.

Self-Reflection

What may be blocking your equanimity or shunyata? (Hint: Our ego is often a culprit, manifesting itself in various ways.)

Where do you try to control the uncontrollable?

Where can you let go?

Practice

Start your morning with at least five minutes of meditation each day.

Incorporate sacred pauses throughout your day.

Choose one day each week to "let go" (for example, "letting go Wednesdays"). Let go of everything you can during that day.

Allow it to be your mantra for that day each week.

Write down any insights you have at the end of the day.

11

The Wisdom of Impermanence

"Everything is in process. Everything—every tree, every blade of grass, all the animals, insects, human beings, buildings, the animate and the inanimate—is always changing, moment to moment."

-Pema Chodron

Life is unpredictable. It feels at times as if we are on shifting sands, and that's because we are. We try to gain some control, or predictability, in many ways. We have been taught since childhood that if we go to college, find a good job, meet the right mate, then all will be well. For any of us who have lived long enough, we know that our plans may easily (or sometimes painstakingly slowly) go awry. Many people "wake up" in mid-life, surprised at what they find, and say to themselves "What happened? Who am I? What is my life about?"

We attempt to build security from the outside in. Mindfulness teaches us to build it from the inside out. By learning to connect with our inner strength and wisdom, we find solid ground regardless of the chaos whirling around us. Rather than feeling like a leaf whipping around in the wind, as many of us do at times, we learn to become the tree, strong and graceful, grounded with deep roots. The tree feels the wind, is affected by the wind, and sways due to the wind, but it is strong and grounded. There is an underpinning of equanimity. In mindfulness, we become like the tree. It can be helpful to picture yourself as the tree when chaos abounds in your life, reminding yourself that your practice has a cumulative effect and will be there to support you when you need it the most.

Regrettably, many people abandon their practice, thus abandoning themselves, when life becomes busy or difficult. This is the very time to become still and quiet, accessing a deeper organic wisdom, divine guidance revealing itself through your own intuition. As Albert Einstein explains, "The significant problems cannot be solved at the same level of thinking with which we created them." And yet, we often reach into the old toolbox, using the very same unskillful strategies we used before we were exposed to these teachings. The more faithful you are to the practice, the more it will serve you in your time of need. If you only practice sometimes, you will feel inner strength and wisdom sometimes. One teacher suggests that we cultivate the attitude of a love affair with our meditation practice rather than seeing it as a discipline. This reframe has helped numerous students. When we feel we "should" do something, it carries the essence of deprivation, and we resist it. When we practice out of love, it carries the energy of delight, and we look forward to it.

The Buddha taught the lesson of the eight worldly winds:

Pleasure and Pain

Gain and Loss

Praise and Blame

Fame and Shame

We are intensely attached to the experiences of pleasure, gain, praise, and fame. We are also negatively attached (aversion) to the fear of pain, loss, blame, and shame. These attachments within us can be so strong that we lose our way. Some people will do anything to experience the former and avoid the latter, even compromise their values, their visions, and their authentic selves. The Buddha reminds us that we cannot escape the eight worldly winds.

Life may be going along well, and then you unexpectedly get a diagnosis of ill health, your mate decides he or she no longer wants to be with you, your company lays you off, you lose the money you invested in the stock market, or you lose someone you love to death. The media at large perpetuates the notion, that if you drive a certain car, buy particular real estate, or look a certain way, then all will be well. We are constantly bombarded by ads that guide us toward consuming more, our futile attempts at "buying security." This feeds the illusion of permanence, of being able to finally arrive. In truth, this cannot actually happen.

We may enjoy our blessings and good fortune. The teachings simply point to the suffering inherent in becoming overly identified with, and thus overly attached, to externals. If we equate who we are with any externals, what happens to our sense of self when we lose our money, our job, our appearance? Life is constantly shifting. The old adage "This too shall pass" refers both to the sorrows and the joys of our lives. If there is anything we can rely on, it is change. And sometimes it takes our breath away.

(Angela) When my youngest sister died tragically in a car accident at age twenty-six, I felt shattered and literally unearthed. My world was turned upside down. Nothing made sense or mattered to me. My heart was broken. I was in tremendous anguish. I developed vertigo as a result of the deep grief and stress. Not surprisingly, I found that meditation was the number one treatment recommended for vertigo by many different types of holistic practitioners. And while my heart still hurts and, at times, I sink into immense sadness, I know that along with the love and care of my dear friends and family, I can rely on my practice to help me ride these waves, to assist me in facing and tolerating the intensity of my emotions and eventually finding ground again.

Peter and Mary were living the good life. They had a strong marriage, happy and successful children, financial security, and an enticing vision of sailing around the world after retirement. Just before they were to retire, Peter had a heart attack and was diagnosed with congestive heart failure. He was forced into early retirement. Not much later, Mary's company went bankrupt and her 401K went along with it. At the same time, the stock market crashed, and they lost a substantial amount of money. Their vision of after sailing around the world was slipping away. However, Peter and Mary had been on the mindfulness path for a year when this occurred. Although shaken and disappointed, they were still able to see their many blessings. They eventually acclimated to their new situation, finding ways to downsize and still enjoy the fruits of their labor in retirement. Although they did not sail around the world, they did some sailing nearby and found other activities to enjoy together. They felt their practice held their marriage together, allowing an internal sense of safety, even as their external world took on a completely different form.

Mindfulness does not suggest that we forego finding a wonderful mate or getting an education. These teachings simply encourage us to release our deep attachments to having it all go our way. Our attachment to the positive, while resisting the negative, causes us tremendous suffering on top of life's pain.

Life includes all of the 10,000 joys and 10,000 sorrows. We learn to hold it all loosely and concurrently. As we prepare for life externally, we can also prepare internally, creating ground for ourselves, cultivating support and equanimity during the difficult times. These teachings point to a better way of relating to impermanence, relaxing into whatever is arising, so that we may surf the waves with clarity, inner strength, and an abiding calm.

Self-Reflection

In what ways are you holding on too tightly?

Where are you overly-identified with externals?

Where can you loosen your grip?

What strategies are you using to attempt control of the uncontrollable?

How might you be creating self-imposed suffering through attachment to external security? How can you cultivate internal stability?

What are your patterns in relation to the eight worldly winds?

How can you work with your attachment and aversion to the eight worldly winds?

Practice

Practice using a "light touch" with the eight worldly winds in your life. Breathe through the discomfort of change. Congratulate yourself when you skillfully navigate change, honoring your successes.

12

Working with Our Thoughts

"The first step for us in working with the storytelling mind is to notice the endless stream of thoughts and commentary that plays along with our experience."
–*Jack Kornfield*

Scientists say that we have 12,000 thoughts per day. Some have even recently reported as many as 64,000. That's a lot of thinking. And most of these thoughts are recurrent! We rarely think new thoughts, and yet, we often review them over and over to arrive at something new. We believe that wisdom lies somewhere in this review. Even when we are physically still, we can be quite busy in our heads. You may have had the experience of thinking through a problem, trying to find a solution, and yet none appears. This is often referred to as "analysis paralysis."

In the corporate world, "thinking outside the box" became hugely popular as a strategy for better business. Working as corporate trainers and executive coaches, we observed that when an employee brings the heart, body, and spirit to an issue, the solutions found are much richer and longer-lasting. We are a society that has overutilized the brain, especially in service of linear, goal-oriented processes. In the progressive business magazine

Fast Company, the reader finds successful executives now meditating, doing yoga, taking naps, and participating in body-oriented work as a way to stay fresh and on the cutting edge. In the January 2011 edition of Shambhala Sun magazine, several interviewees including a physician, a police officer, a law school professor and a set of parents, all cite the benefits of integrating mindfulness into their lives and the resulting clarity and productivity they experience.

Our thoughts are very powerful. They can empower us or disempower us. It is important to become conscious of what you think on a daily basis, what you tell yourself. For example, if you find yourself backed up on deadlines, and you keep telling yourself "I can't do this," odds are, you will not be able to do it. On the other hand, you can say to yourself, "I can handle this. Just take one step at a time." This is a more empowering, skillful way to approach the pressure of the day, and the results will likely be much better. We are talking to ourselves all day long (some of us out loud!), so it behooves us to bring these thought patterns to conscious light to make sure that what we are saying is in our best interest. As R.D. Laing states, "The range of what we think and do is limited by what we fail to notice."

When we practice listening deeply to our thoughts, we notice the top layer. Then we listen more deeply to thoughts below this. And then we listen even more deeply to the whispered thoughts, barely perceptible, but present and powerful all the same. For example, when Andrea's car broke down on the interstate, she had a complete meltdown waiting for the tow truck. Her first wave of thoughts was common: "I can't believe this is happening to me." (non-acceptance and personalizing). "This is probably going to cost a bundle. It may be my engine. If I need a new engine, I might as well get a new car. I can't afford a new car. Without my car, I won't be able to get to work. And I can't rely on anyone to help me get there." (catastrophizing).

The next wave of thoughts underneath the first wave: "Why does this always happen to me? I am such a mess. I'm never going to be able to rise above, to find solid footing in this world. No one is going to help me." As she listens even more deeply, Andrea's whispered thoughts say "I am all alone in this world. No one will help me because I am not worthy or loved. I really don't want to be here anymore." Andrea begins to explode mentally and emotionally, not because of her car breaking down, but because of what she has told herself within a matter of five minutes.

We have these types of ongoing conversations with ourselves all day every day. As we become more aware of our thoughts, we can intervene and create more empowering alternatives. In traditional psychology, we call this our "explanatory style." Andrea could have taken a sacred pause, breathing through the discomfort she was feeling, and resting in the ambiguity of "beginner's mind." Andrea was running a storyline about this incident and herself that was destructive. The truth was that she did not know what was wrong with the car. In the end, she did have to replace the alternator, but she did not have to replace the car. By listening more deeply, Andrea realized that she needed to work on her feelings of isolation and unworthiness.

Sometimes, when we have an emotion or a bodily sensation, we run a storyline that can be harmful to us. In our work at Cancer Wellness, we witness cancer patients working with this issue on a regular basis. Even after a person has recovered from the trauma of a cancer diagnosis and treatment, the fearful thoughts linger. A sensation in the body is often immediately questioned, "Is the cancer back?" Or it may sound more like "the cancer IS back!" even though it is not. As they work through the guidance mindfulness offers, they can pause, breathe, and redirect their thinking. As they become more conscious of these fearful thoughts, they begin to change them to more helpful thought patterns.

The ability of the brain to be changed was postulated as far back as 1890 by psychologist Dr. William James. James is quoted as saying, "The greatest discovery of my generation is that a human being can alter his life by altering his attitudes." Recently, the work of Dan Siegel, M.D., Jack Kornfield, Ph.D., and Norman Doidge, M.D., definitively points to the neuroplasticity of the brain. This exciting evidence allows us to understand the brain's malleability. We can change our experience by reprogramming this three-pound super computer.

When we focus on positive thinking repetitively, the brain rewires itself. This is not unlike exercise, whereby activity and repetition lead to a literal physical shift; in the realm of thinking, this means a change in the structure of the brain. An affirmative loop is created in our thinking patterns. Also, research by Mark George, M.D. (Medical University of South Carolina) at the National Institutes of Health, and his colleagues, demonstrated that happy, hopeful thoughts have an overall calming effect on the brain. Negative thoughts inflame brain areas often involved with depression and anxiety. The critical question here is: What experience do you want to create?

When working with our thoughts, we must question the stories we are telling ourselves. Have you ever had the experience of thinking one thing about a person or event and later finding out that it wasn't accurate? In reality, the "truth" was the exact opposite of what you had "known?" Or have you had the experience of a misfortune soon turning out to be a blessing? We re-engage negative thinking even after having these insights because we would rather be "in the know" and sometimes miserable than sit in the uncomfortable ambiguity of "beginner's mind."

Beginnner's mind encourages us to be curious rather than clever. Being "in the know" is a way for us to try to gain control, but it sets us up for unnecessary, self-imposed suffering. Even if something bad is arising, worry does not helps us or the situation. At best, worry depletes us of mental, emotional, and even physical energy. Mindfulness teaches us that the ability to sit in ambiguity, although we often resist it due to a sense of losing control, helps us reduce our suffering. When we indulge in disempowering thinking, we strengthen that muscle, and when we indulge in empowering thinking, we strengthen that muscle.

> There is an old, Native-American tale from the Cherokee tribe. The story is a conversation between a young warrior and his elder. "Grandfather," the adolescent asked, "after such a tragedy, what do we do?"
>
> "Inside me," said the Grandfather, "I feel two wolves fighting. One wolf is angry, full of vengeance, and aggression. The other wolf is gentle, full of love, compassion, and forgiveness."
>
> "Which wolf will win, Grandfather?"
>
> "The one which I feed will be the one who wins."

This legend directs us to the poignant idea that what we think about and focus on grows larger, and thus, becomes our experience.

In meditation, we realize the transitory nature of thoughts. We are not our thoughts. Thoughts are not concrete. They are fluid. They form and pass away. Then another thought comes. In meditation, we move into the gap between thoughts. We expand that gap more and more. This translates into our daily life as well. The more we meditate and redirect our thinking, the more control we'll have over our thoughts and experience. As Jack Kornfield teaches, "You can't stop the waves but you can learn to surf."

Self-Reflection

What are your recurring thought patterns? (worry, what if's, planning)

What suffering might they bring? To you? To others?

What choices can you make to support rather than harm yourself with your thought process?

Write a more empowering thought to one recurrent negative thought.

Practice

Intervene on yourself once a day when you catch the wheels of negative thinking turning. As soon as you notice this thought process in play, replace the negative thinking either with a beginner's mind statement (I don't know what may happen) or with positive thinking.

Try telling yourself a different story than the one you're telling. Write a few stories, one similar but slightly altered, one more empowering, and one that is the opposite of your original story. Notice if you find any truth or wisdom in the other stories

13

Working with Our Emotions

"Emotions are actually necessary information, which ultimately helps the process of fighting disease and healing."
-Roger Dafter

Carol and John were in the middle of their third couple's session with us. They had come to learn better communication and conflict resolution skills. We were discussing a difficult issue around disciplining their four-year old son who has a learning disability. Carol was tearful but trying not to cry or speak while John fumed and said things to Carol that he would soon regret. When we inquired about how each was feeling, they described their thoughts, opinions and positions. Carol and John were both bright, sensitive people and yet were unable to identify and verbalize their emotions. They often found themselves stuck here and unable to move forward.

Tracy was a clerk who was held at gunpoint in a convenience store robbery. We met her when Dennis was called in to debrief the employees. She initially presented very calmly after the incident. She came to see us to address her lack of motivation and inability to focus as she had before the robbery. Weeks passed before she could acknowledge her anger, fear, and sadness.

Chris was diagnosed with multiple sclerosis. His anxiety progressed to the point of debilitating him. Although his mind and body currently functioned well, his fear overwhelmed his ability to get up in the morning and go to work. He no longer enjoyed his hobbies or time with friends. He worried obsessively about the future, terrorizing himself with "what ifs."

It takes courage to acknowledge our full range of emotions. We feel more comfortable with certain emotions. Some of us feel most comfortable leading with anger, and that's what we express, even if we feel confused, lonely, or scared. Some of us lead with sadness, and we cry whether we're feeling sad, angry, or scared. For the most part, we have not been taught to experience and express our emotions.

We ask our clients and students to practice identifying emotions. We provide them with a feelings chart like the abbreviated one at the end of this chapter. This allows them to understand various categories and intensity levels of emotions and encourages them to express their internal experience verbally. Research shows that a more sophisticated emotional vocabulary enhances the immune system and that a lack of this vocabulary, a condition called alexithymia, harms the immune system.

The term alexithymia was created in 1972 by psychiatrist Peter Sifneos, M.D., to mean the inability to express feelings with words. With "emotional literacy," the health of the individual improves. Numerous studies cited and summarized by Tomas Uher in Activitas Nervosa Superior (The Journal For Neurocognitive Research, 2010) lend supportive evidence to the relationship between alexithymia and dysfunction of the immune system. As homework for most of our clients, we ask them to identify one emotion a day as precisely as possible rather than applying broad labels such as "mad, sad, glad, etc."

We ask clients to practice "being" with an emotion. Many people ask us what this means. Being with your emotion means simply experiencing it, without running a storyline. Just noticing the sensation of the emotion. We guide clients to sense where they feel it in their bodies. Then we ask them to describe it, the texture and the sensation. We ask them to bring their hands to that part of the body, if appropriate, and just notice, not clinging to or judging the emotion. We then ask them to direct the breath to that area. This often gives a sense of spaciousness around the emotion, making it more palatable to experience. It also helps the client become aware of the emotion's fluidity.

Realizing that we are not our emotions, and that all emotions are fluid, gives us more courage to face what we are feeling. As we practice bringing awareness and breath to the emotion, it may begin to change. And as we sit with and experience the next emotion, it may morph again into another emotion. In his CD Mindfulness and Psychotherapy (2006), Thich Nhat Hanh uses the analogy of the sun to the flower. The sun does not go around the flower. It penetrates the flower, causing beautiful growth and transformation. Likewise, when we bring our mindful awareness and breath to our emotions, we heal and transform ourselves.

It is tempting to label emotions as "good" or "bad," but it is more skillful to honor our full humanity by owning our full range of emotions. Identifying and experiencing this full range of emotions differs from residing in them. You may have met people in your life who seem to live in their anger or sadness. John and Carol, the couple at the beginning of this chapter, were two such people. As they worked with mindfuness techniques, and honored a broader range of emotions, they were released from this limited way of being, expressing and relating.

In Buddhist and yogic philosophy, the Sanskrit word "klesha" is described as an intense emotion that leads to great suffering. Have you ever experienced your anger getting away from you? Sometimes it's described as "going from 0 to 100 in 60 seconds." This is an example of a klesha. As we grow in self-awareness, we begin to identify the first glimmer of emotion; perhaps it's the tightness in the shoulders or feeling the stomach drop for a millisecond. When we notice the emotion arising, we can intervene before we reach 100. We can choose to respond *skillfully* rather than *react* in the habitual patterns of our past. As soon as we notice the emotion, we can pause and breathe, acknowledging what is occurring within us. We can respond with wisdom, causing ourselves and others less suffering.

Research also shows that the regulation of emotions, especially negative ones, is affected by regular meditation. Studies by Brefczynski-Lewis et al. (2007) show that meditation influences our emotional circuitry, primarily in the amygdala. This allows more control over the intensity of our emotions and our responses to them. We can withstand greater emotional intensity in ourselves and others without distancing or being overwhelmed.

Dr. Jon Kabat-Zinn, University of Massachusetts, has conducted other research on emotional circuitry and meditation. His studies indicate that meditation enlarges the brain's prefrontal cerebral cortex, enabling us to manage stress better.

These studies suggest that, with consistent meditation, we seem to have more control over the intensity of our emotions and our responses to them. Events and people that previously triggered us no longer elicit the same destructive reactions. In mindfulness, we call these triggers our teachers. Teachers elicit strong reactions in us and provide us with opportunities for growth.

Matthew Lieberman, Ph.D., of UCLA, in 2007 documented that when we identify and speak our feelings aloud, there is a noticeable decrease in the amygdala (fear region of the brain) and an increase in the prefrontal cortex (on/off switch for emotional decision-making). This translates into having less of a chronic stress response in the body. This is due to inhibition of adrenaline and other stress hormones. Identifying emotions relaxes the physiology and allows for better health.

But what are the health implications if we *don't* recognize and release our emotions? Alicia A. Grandey, Ph.D., of Penn State University (2000) explains that "The physiological 'bottling up' of emotions taxes the body over time by overworking the cardiovascular and nervous systems and weakening the immune system." She goes on to say that "Research has linked the inhibition of emotions to a variety of physical illnesses, including high blood pressure, heart disease, and cancer. Grandey also suggests that "Inability to express negative emotions may be one of the strongest predictors of cancer."

When we choose to work with our emotions in a mindful way, we strengthen the skillful part of ourselves, and according to the research, we strengthen our health, too. Each time we lose control, we cause suffering to ourselves and others, and we strengthen that unskillful part of ourselves. The choice is ours. This can be difficult and scary work, and you may choose to work with a therapist, a coach, or a teacher to explore the broader range of emotional identification and expression.

As Tracy learned to befriend herself and all her emotions, she was able to honor and express her deepest feelings about being held at gunpoint. Arriving at these insights required "emotional excavation," the willingness to dig deeply. She became more emotionally integrated and happier.

As Chris was able to identify the terrifying storylines he was telling himself about his diagnosis, he could change his thought process. Meditation showed Chris the fluidity of his thoughts and emotions, that they arise and pass away. He learned to honor his fear when it arose, without clinging to or rejecting it. As he did this, he found more spaciousness within and around his emotions, making them easier to face. He reduced his anxiety, got back to work, and eventually helped others diagnosed with multiple sclerosis.

Self-Reflection

Which emotions do you lead with and which do you reject or judge? Why?

What did you learn about emotions in childhood and how does that impact you now as an adult?

What storylines are you telling yourself? Are they helping or harming?

What are your emotional patterns? How are they connected to your mental and behavioral patterns?

Practice

Use the chart below to identify how you are feeling at least once a day.

When asked to share their emotions, clients often start with broad ones such as frustration. This requires less work and vulnerability. In a process of emotional excavation, clients are guided into a deeper exploration of feelings. Frequently hidden below anger, for example, lies a form of fear or sadness. This excavation enables otherwise shielded emotions to ascend to the surface. In the conscious light, they can be addressed and healed.

Feelings Chart

"I feel ________"

HAPPY	SAD	ANGRY	SCARED	CONFUSE
Content	Down	Annoyed	Nervous	Uncertain
Satisfied	Discouraged	Irritated	Apprehensive	Puzzled
Excited	Depressed	Disappointed	Panicky	Bewildered
Encouraged	Lonely	Resentful	Unsure	Torn
Eager	Upset	Furious	Afraid	Conflicted
Glad	Hurt	Offended	Insecure	Distrustful
Pleased	Helpless	Agitated	Worried	Skeptical
Elated	Guilty	Disgusted	Terrified	Mixed-up
Light-hearted	Melancholy	Miffed	Frightened	Disorientec
Loved	Gloomy	Incensed	Intimidated	Mystified
Blissful	Miserable	Irate	Threatened	Bothered
Delightful	Hopeless	Exasperated	Petrified	Lost
Ecstatic	Blue	Hostile	Unclear	Uncomfort
Overjoyed	Drained	Uptight	Alarmed	Disorganiz
Amused	Heartbroken	Bitter	Tense	Muddled

14

Working with Our Bodies

"Our bodies are the gateway to enlightenment."
-Reginald Ray

Our bodies are amazing. Working with cancer patients at Cancer Wellness at Piedmont Hospital highlights this truth every day. Our bodies have an immense capacity to heal and restore. At a holistic conference in Florida, Belleruth Naperstak reminded us that our bodies are our oldest allies. They have been with us through it all. No one else can be in our bodies but us. And yet, we don't often treat ourselves as well as we could. Learning to care for our bodies as the precious and unique gifts that they are is key to reaping the benefits they offer.

The old adage "Our biology is our biography" reminds us that the body holds much wisdom and many keys for healing. The Buddha taught that if we could master our bodies, we could master life. In traditional medicine, it was previously believed that "thinking" was housed in our brains only. We now understand through the research of Candace Pert, Ph.D. in Molecules of Emotion: The Science Behind Mind-Body Medicine (1999), that we have as many neuroreceptors around our heart and in our gut as in our brain. Our "gut instinct" or "calling of the heart" is more than just a saying. The cells in our immune system communicate with the brain, which communicates with the heart, which communicates with the cells in the gut, and so on. Dr. Pert scientifically establishes the existence of the dynamic information network between the mind and the body, the body and the emotions. This was an unprecedented breakthrough, substantiating the "mind-body" connection.

As yoga teachers, we know there is much to be learned from being fully present in our bodies. Unfortunately, our culture has perpetuated the destructive habit of objectifying the body. Body image issues, anorexia and bulimia, and chronic dieting have become increasingly prominent. Current research in this field shows that the average girl goes on her first diet by second grade, often placed on it by her mother. Childhood obesity documentaries and the billion dollar adult weight loss industry are signs that we have become out-of-sync with our physical selves.

Learning to love the body we are in, exactly as it is today, is a part of making friends with ourselves, a starting point for healing. From a place of self-love, compassion, and clarity, we can create an intention to change and heal our physical selves. We cannot do this from a place of self-hatred, self-judgment, and perfectionism. If we send messages like these, our bodies and immune systems will respond in kind. We may be able to create an illusion of what we want (i.e., a certain weight). While this addresses the exterior concerns, it does not create the comprehensive health that brings happiness and peace.

In our work, we witness clients addressing their physical concerns while overlooking their overall health. Mary was intent on keeping up her appearance. She maintained an ideal weight, received regular botox injections, and always looked great. However, she did not exercise or eat well, so she developed high blood pressure.

Our bodies carry much wisdom. When we practice deep listening to our bodies, we find a guide to the answers we are seeking. One yoga student, Jill, developed a chronic neck pain she could not seem to shake. We worked on it through asanas (yoga postures) and pranayama (breathwork). The pain would subside, soon to return again. One day we asked her the question, "What in your life is a pain in the neck?" We asked her to go home and write about it. When she returned to yoga class, she had a long list of "pain in the neck" life items. The one that seemed to jump off the page, though, was her mother. Her mother had recently moved closer to Jill and expected her to visit more often than Jill wanted. As we dialogued about this new life dilemma, Jill realized her need to set limits around visitation. Her neck pain soon disappeared.

Kevin attended a yoga and meditation retreat we facilitated. Kevin knows the truth about the body's wisdom. He told the group that he was surprised when he had a heart attack a few years previous. He began to investigate, with his therapist, the emotional connections to his physical illness. He soon realized that his heart had literally been breaking for years due to his son's troubles. He knew that in order to fully heal, he must work through his grief and release his son to his own path. Kahlil Gibran suggests that "These children are not our own. They come through us and to us, but they ultimately belong to God." Incorporating these kinds of truths leads to a healthier body and a more peaceful spirit.

Our bodies can also help guide our decisions. When a client seems torn between two conflicting options, we often ask them to close their eyes and picture the first option, noticing any sensations in their bodies. We then ask them to picture the second option, again noticing what arises physically. Terry was trying to decide if he should go to his company holiday party or stay home with his partner for the evening. He repeatedly reviewed the pros and cons of each in his head. We asked him to drop down into his body and picture each of the two scenarios. He described tightness in his chest when picturing himself at the party and a visceral sense of relief when imagining himself at home with his partner. His authentic self, as conveyed by his bodily sensations, guided him towards the second option. Our bodies always tell us the truth when we pay attention.

When a client is feeling deep emotion, we ask him or her to "sit with it" rather than doing anything. We ask the client to drop out of the head (which is running a storyline about the emotion) and into the body, where a felt sense of the emotion can be directly accessed and experienced. We may ask "Where in your body are you feeling the emotion?" We then guide the client to place their hands on that part of the body, if appropriate, and breathe into it. As the client breathes through the emotion, it may dissipate or morph into another emotion. This process helps them tolerate uncomfortable emotions and reminds them that emotions are fluid and transitory. Eventually all emotions pass. We are not our emotions. And we are not our bodies.

The ego would have us believe that we are our bodies. That we are our appearances, our maladies, our strengths or weaknesses. When we overly identify with our bodies, we suffer. The Buddha taught that we all go through bodily changes. We all age and eventually die. If we cling too tightly to our bodies, we suffer greatly around this inevitable reality. There is a deeper "I" that lives within, a part of us that some call our true nature, the witness, the compassionate presence, our higher self, our deeper identity, our soul. This is what the body houses.

How can we care for our bodies? Research in integrative medicine shows us that nutrition and exercise are very powerful contributors to our wellness. Thierry Bouillet, M.D., an oncologist and head of The Radiation Institute at University Hospital in Bobigny, France, as well as Medical Director at the Avicenna Medical Center and an expert in Sports Medicine, has observed the phenomenal impact of exercise on health. Dr. Bouilett has noticed many fewer cases of cancer among those who are physically active. He also has discerned that cancer patients who are active have significantly fewer recurrences than those who do not exercise. Exercise reduces adipose tissue, which can act as a storage site for carcinogenic toxins. Furthermore, exercise balances hormones and brings them into homeostasis. Beyond that, exercise offers many other benefits, including a sense of well-being.

Nutrition's influence on wellness is too extensive to cover here. But examining our diets and modifying the negative elements will improve our health and our outlook. Finding balance with sugar, alcohol, meat, fat, dairy and salt helps tremendously. Eating organic foods and drinking pure water are good practices as well. We don't have to deprive ourselves when eating well. There are many tasty, healthy recipes available now. In her book, Taste and Savor: Delicious Healthy Recipes & Tasty Wine Tips (2010), our friend, chef Nancy Waldeck, offers numerous quick and easy healthy recipes for better living. This is the body we've been given – "the body is the temple" – and moderation and balance in our diets helps us feel better and live longer.

Also, the way in which we communicate with our bodies is important. Messages of self-love and acceptance create an enhanced immune system while messages of judgment and rejection create a diminished immune system (Pert, 1997). Caring for our bodies includes treating them with kindness, respect, and honor. Research shows that mindfulness practice assists our bodies by enhancing the immune system, reducing inflammation, regulating blood pressure, reducing cortisol, and reducing pain. Also, nurturing physical activities, like yoga, tai chi, and massage, are integral to physical health and wellness.

Self-Reflection

What does it feel like to be fully present in your body?

What messages does your body have for you?

What physical ailments do you have? List them. Ask yourself "What in my life is……"(i.e. hemorrhoids = "a pain in the butt")

How can I commit to better, more comprehensive care of my body?

Practice

Lie down and make yourself comfortable. Remain awake during this process. Find a place of calm awareness within. Practice a body scan from toe to head, bringing your awareness to each part of your body, noticing what is arising. (Note: You may use the meditation CD that we have available on our site as a guide if you wish.) This practice allows you to cultivate a deeper relationship with your body and its wisdom.
It also teaches your mind/body how to calm and quiet itself.

15

Self-Love, Self-Honor, Self-Compassion

"You yourself, as much as anybody in the entire universe, deserve your love and affection."

-Buddha

Only a fortunate few were taught these concepts as children. For many of us, these are foreign ideas. They are often equated with selfishness or self-absorption. We have learned to put ourselves on the back burner. As a result, we become overextended, resentful, and disconnected. The Buddha taught that it is skillful to take delight in oneself, to acknowledge and reflect on the good that is within. What do you like about yourself? What makes you happy about you? Acknowledging self-love is essential to your health and happiness.

At the end of every yoga class, we ask participants to take a moment to remember their true nature and to acknowledge self- love. This is a healing practice, reminding us that we are worthy and deserving of our own love. We often send so much out to those around us that there is nothing left for us. This may be a part of how martyrdom develops. We feel bereft within when we have given everything away. A part of self-love is acknowledging our feelings, desires, and needs and then, skillfully expressing them to those around us.

When Julie was a child, her mother often called her selfish. Julie was always confused by this and knew that she was not selfish. In fact she was often quite the opposite, even caring for others at a very young age. Throughout adulthood, Julie struggled with self-love and self-care. She believed that being needless and wantless was preferable. When Julie expressed a need or a feeling, she was confirmed selfish in her own mind. Through therapy, Julie learned to claim her needs and wants as valid. She learned to love herself and care for herself. She learned that it is acceptable to be selfish at times. She also learned to forgive her mother for the wounding, knowing that her mother was wounded in her own way.

The wounds of our parents often get projected onto us and may block our self-love. We then carry these wounds of "not enough." Some of these messages are projected loudly, others more subtly. We buy into these messages as truth because they enter our brains at a time when we are very vulnerable to our parents' (and others') messages about who we are.

Metta is a Sanskrit word for "loving-kindness." In metta meditation, we offer loving-kindness to ourselves first, to a benefactor, to a loved one, to a stranger, to a difficult person, and then to all living beings. We start with ourselves first. Similar to the emergency instructions on a plane, we put on our facemask first before helping others. Participants commonly have resistance to offering loving-kindness to self first. It is awkward, unusual. They also resist receiving loving-kindness, finding it difficult to open their hearts to themselves. If this is the case, we ask them to focus on metta only for themselves, for a week or a month. This allows self-love to penetrate down to the cellular level, until they embody this feeling and become comfortable with it.

Opening our hearts to ourselves is essential to our well-being. Sharon Salzberg is an expert on this subject, and in her book Loving-Kindness: The Revolutionary Art of Happiness (1997), she describes the process of many master teachers who have struggled with self-love. Their teachers often suggest that they meditate solely on metta for self. Sometimes this takes months. *We had the good fortune of retreating with Sharon at the Drepung*

Loseling Monastery in Atlanta for two days. We focused primarily on metta for ourselves. After those two days, we felt uplifted, centered, and nourished.

What we turn our attention and awareness towards has the power to hurt or to heal. Much of what we are consuming through the media, conversations, and readings is hurtful to us. We take in messages of anger, defeat, and "not enough." If we consume these messages on a regular basis, we feel down, defeated, and disconnected. Likewise, if we focus on consuming messages of love, kindness, and personal power, we feel inspired, happy, and connected. Sometimes, we have to put in a little more effort to find positive messages, but in the end, it is well worth the energy to take in that which heals us.

Due to being so busy on the treadmill of life, we often forget that the wisdom of self-love is accessible. We tend to slip into unconsciousness at times, often called "auto-pilot." The thirteenth century Sufi poet Rumi beckons us to remain awake in his poem "Don't Go Back to Sleep" (Barks, 2004). When we are awake and aware, we remember who we really are, our true nature, and our inherent lovability. Then we are seduced back into the busyness of life, slowly forgetting again. This is an ancient universal issue; the potential for slipping back into sleepwalking through life. When we do so, we unconsciously return to a place within in which we don't love or honor ourselves.

An indispensable part of honoring and loving oneself is recognizing one's needs and feelings. Sometimes our needs and feelings are in direct conflict with someone else's needs and feelings. Some of us fall into a pattern of codependency where we regularly put others first, relegating our own needs and feelings to the back burner. After a protracted period of doing this, we become overextended, resentful, fatigued, and burned out. *In a writing class called "Writing for Recovery" facilitated by Angela at Cancer Wellness, participants often write poetry based on the theme of the class.* In one class, they worked with the theme of self-love and self-honor. Below are several poems that participants wrote and shared with our community.

Affirmation For 2009

Too often I carry a backpack
Filled with the stones named
should, must, guilt, duty.

That pack is a very heavy
And unnecessary burden.

I will replace those stones
with feathers named
self-care, joy, happiness and love.

-Becky

SAYING NO!

Saying NO! isn't easy.
Convincing the hearer you really mean it
Is even harder
Yet saying NO! to others is often saying
YES! To yourself.
NO! frees you from the shackles of
Unwanted tasks.
NO! says I have something more compelling to do.
NO! says I must honor my own needs.
NO! says I am putting me at the top of my
"to do" list.
NO! to you is YES! to me.

-Becky

Flashback: Who's That?

I remember picking up the phone on the second ring.

Now I let the machine take the call.

I'm painting.

I remember when I use to get to the office a half hour earlier.

Now I get there in the nick of time.

I was meditating.

I remember when I would stay late at the office.

Now I leave at five o'clock on the dot.

I have a writing class to go to.

I remember putting friends and family first.

Now I prioritize them.

There's an art show I want to see

A concert I want to attend

A weekend trip I want to take

My favorite author is signing his/her new bestseller at my favorite bookstore.

I remember not living fully.

Now it's my mandate to live as full as I can get.

- Kevin

As the eldest child of three and a "parentified" child, Constance grew up thinking that it was her job to ensure everyone else's well-being. She rarely thought of herself as important, always believing she could endure whatever occurred in her life. She was a cheerleader. She listened. She advocated. She ran to and fro. She assumed the role of the strong one in the family, and then eventually with friends, and with mates. Therefore, she often did not get her own needs met.

Constance was blocking that possibility by not expressing her own internal experiences. Inside she often felt isolated and unloved. She trained everyone around her that she did not have feelings and needs, that she would always be there for them, and that reciprocity was not necessary. As she worked her way out of this pattern, sometimes not as gracefully as she would like, she felt more balanced, nourished, fulfilled, and peaceful. She had to love herself enough to step out of a comfort zone, albeit an unsatisfying one, to care for herself, and then to convey her feelings and needs to those around her.

As you begin to set boundaries in your own life, some people may not support you. Be patient with yourself and others as you practice this new way of being. Those who are meant to stay in your life will remain, and those who are not will move on.

Boundaries are fundamental to self-love and self-honor. Some of us have lived so long without boundaries that "saying no" feels awkward. We like how Becky describes that saying "no" to others sometimes means saying "yes" to yourself. Saying "yes" to ourselves sometimes is skillful, reflecting on what we need and desire. Kevin's decisions to nourish himself, rather than meet unrealistic outside expectations, permitted him to claim a new quality of life that allowed him to feel happy, enriched, and whole. You may feel guilty and uncomfortable as you begin this part of your healing process. Stay with the feelings (see chapter on Emotions), and breathe through them as you move towards a more empowered and whole way of life.

Deep Listening is a practice that Thich Nhat Hanh advocates as a part of self-love. We often are not quiet or still enough to hear ourselves. We guide people through deep listening practice by asking them to become still first, finding their breath, and then listening to their thoughts, emotions, bodies, and spirits, moving through each of these areas. Sometimes we spend more time on one area. Deep listening is not solely listening to the first thing that arises.

When we listen deeply, we penetrate the layers of patterns and defenses to find what really resides within. For example, when a client Karrie, had a conflict with a co-worker, she initially heard only the chatter in her head about who said what to whom. She felt angry. As she listened more deeply, she noticed thoughts like "I wish my co-worker would recognize my contributions and value to this team," as well as emotions of anxiety and uncertainty. As she listened even more deeply, the ache in the pit of her stomach conveyed primal fear and a thought that "I am not safe in the world." From this insight, she worked to transform her internal suffering. If she had stopped at the first level, she may have gotten stuck in her self-righteousness and the drama of the scenario, setting herself up to repeat disempowering patterns. When you engage in deep listening, it may be helpful to write in a journal afterwards to gain greater self-understanding.

Self-Reflection

What do self-love, self-compassion, and self-honor mean to you?

How do they translate into your day-to-day life?

What gets in the way of loving yourself? Perfectionism, comparing, judging, old messages, people, etc.?

What changes would you like to make?

Practice

At the beginning of each day, ask yourself "How can I love and honor myself today?" Choose one way that you will practice for the day: changing the way you talk to yourself, participating in activities and events, changing your mind, having a voice, taking a break, creating boundaries, practicing deep listening, or spending time doing what you love. Many options and avenues to practice are available.

16

Mindful Relationships

"As we learn to look gently and honestly at ourselves, at our thoughts, feelings, emotions, the great stuff and the less than great stuff, we can see that we have built up a lot of barriers to loving others and ourselves."

-Peggy Rowe-Ward and Larry Ward

Satre writes "Hell is other people." A smile in response to Satre's quote is common. We recognize his sentiment as something we ourselves have thought at times. We also recognize that heaven is other people, too. In the words of John Donne, "No man is an island." Thank goodness for other people, and all their differences. Without them, opportunities to grow would be limited. We think we want others to be more like us. In reality, their differences are enriching. What would life really be like if we were married to ourselves, if all of our friends and colleagues thought and acted like us, or if our children were carbon copies?

When confronted with people who think, talk, and behave differently, we can welcome the opportunities to learn and grow. We can ask ourselves, "What is it like to be in relationship with me?" We (Angela and Dennis) often encourage clients to review each of their relationships and write what the relationship may be like for the other person. This exercise never fails to alter the perspective, and more importantly, the heart.

Larry and Peggy Ward wrote Love's Garden: A Guide to Mindful Relationships (2008), a comprehensive and beautifully written book on the lessons and healing power of mindfulness in relationships. *During a retreat with Larry and Peggy, we struggled with various family relationships that created chronic feelings of worry, distress and heartache. When we reached out to various family members to discuss our experiences, we were met with denial, resentment, and alienation. We felt helpless. Although we made a conscious decision to halt our "rescue" attempts, we continued to pray for their greater good, kept them in our daily metta practice, and surrendered the issues to God.*

We continue to offer a steady presence of love and light where we are able, realizing that we, too, have limitations on how much of an impact we can make. In Buddhist psychology, this is considered a "release from codependency." We must allow others to live their lives as they choose, and to suffer the consequences of their actions, as painful as this is to witness. We keep others in our hearts, even when they cause us immense grief, knowing we may be unable to continue frequent contact if we want optimal health.

Relationships tend to generate a lot of feedback. In Buddhist psychology, feedback is considered a rare and precious gift. Ultimately, it is up to us to examine the feedback and determine if it has merit. Relationships sometimes reflect back to us our shortcomings, both perceived and real. We receive feedback, some valid and some invalid, projections of others' wounds and baggage. Because of this, many people avoid true intimacy, even in platonic relationships. They do not reveal their authentic selves, and if anyone gets too close, they inevitably sabotage the relationship. Some are afraid of others seeing their faults, their vulnerabilities, their rough edges. At a subconscious or unconscious level, they do not feel wholly worthy or lovable, so they act defensively and keep barriers in place. However we can continue to love them and see their beauty.

Perhaps you have been hurt, criticized, rejected, or abandoned. You may be more guarded and less trusting as a result. A yoga teacher once said that true friends see the essence of beauty within us, even when we don't appear beautiful. In one soft whisper, they blow away all the rest. This emotional safety and warmth can help us heal our wounds. However, if we continue intimacy-avoidant patterns, we miss the opportunity to have our lovability reflected back to us. When someone loves and accepts us unconditionally, we come home to ourselves. We live in true abundance. When we are that person for others, we strengthen our bodhichitta, our awakened heart-mind.

Expectations can be a real emotional "hook" in relationships. We have many expectations – of others and ourselves. Some are realistic; some are not. Regardless, expectations are a set-up for relationship failure. We often witness clients expecting certain behaviors from others – parents, mates, colleagues - when prior behaviors have been consistently disappointing.

One client, Christen, found this dynamic with her family of origin. Approaching family visits, she would become hopeful, imagining a connection with her parents and siblings that had never occurred previously. During the visit, her family would inevitably behave as they always had, detached and emotionally avoidant. Christen would be disappointed, having formed unrealistic expectations. Upon returning from her visit, she would have what could best be described as an "emotional hangover."

Through mindfulness training, Christen learned that expecting anything different was a set-up for disappointment. Working on acceptance, with clarity and an open heart, was essential for Christen. We suggested she start by clearly communicating her needs to her family, without blame. However, we reminded her that they may continue in the same vein. If they did not alter their behavior, she had choices. She might choose to limit the amount of time she spent at these reunions. She might choose to get a hotel room nearby so that she could leave when she was ready. This type of self-care, combined with setting boundaries was a powerful turning point for her. Although she was distressed, she did not want to lose her family. She learned to love and accept her family of origin as they are while seeking another "family of choice" for emotional connection and other needs. She felt much better, and she was able to keep her family in her life and in her heart.

When we lower our expectations and keep our hearts open, we live more peacefully. This is easier said than done. *We had to change our own expectations in our relationship. Angela expected that Dennis would want the same periods of quiet that she did, and Dennis expected that Angela would be as energetic as he was on Sunday mornings. We learned to modify our expectations of one another, and unexpected pleasant shifts have occurred.* When there is a conflict of needs, it is futile to continue filing the same complaint. Both parties must empathize and compromise if they want a healthy relationship.

We want people to act as we expect. Maya Angelou makes a good point in her statement: "When people show you who they are, believe them." We often ignore this advice, denying patterns of previous behavior. Beginner's mind, "curiosity," is helpful in loosening our grip on expectations. When we see people as they are, we can make choices as Christen did. We can communicate our needs, alter our behavior, and make alternative plans for engagement. If necessary, we can remove people from our lives in order to protect our well-being.

Mental models of others can be an issue. We sometimes attempt to concretize people rather than seeing them as the fluid entities they are. Our egos tell us that people should fit a certain expectation – look a particular way, behave a certain way, or speak in a specific way. We are then blocked from seeing the richness and depth others bring to our experience. It behooves us all to examine our own mental models, what we are expecting, consciously and subconsciously.

Mindful communication is central to healthy, happy relationships. The ways in which we deliver messages are as important as the messages themselves. We can convey our thoughts, even difficult ones, with an open heart and a respectful tone. We can also listen to others' messages with an open mind, examining them for possible merit and validity. We each want to be heard and understood. Stephen Covey suggests "Seek first to understand, then to be understood." Working on our own communication process, around delivery and receptivity, rather than repeatedly reviewing the content, can help our relationships grow and heal. You may find it beneficial to consult a third party for coaching through difficult conversations.

Self-Reflection

We can water positive or negative seeds of perceptions as we assess others. What is your tendency?

Do you give people the benefit of the doubt? Do you get stuck in being "against" others or in judgmental mind?

What patterns tend to characterize your relationships?

What is it like for others to be in relationship with you?

Practice

For one day, try to take the other person's perspective, whether that person is the cashier at your local store, your child, your mate, or anyone else. Practice softening your heart towards them, connecting with their humanity – their desire to be happy and peaceful in life. Consider what it is like for them to be in a relationship with you. Start one day a week, build to a couple of days, then eventually try it for an entire week. Note insights you have along the way.

17

Grief

““We are not human beings having a spiritual experience. We are spiritual beings having a human experience.”

-Teilhard de Chardin

During the writing of this book we have endured two tragic losses. First, we lost Angela's youngest sister, Charly, in a tragic car accident. Four months later to the day, Dennis' mother died from congestive heart failure. The impact of these events felt like a tidal wave pushing us to the floor of the ocean, causing us to feel disoriented and unable to breathe at times. Our mindfulness practices, along with the love and care of so many, helped us to endure and move through our grief, baby step by baby step. There have been days when it has been difficult to get out of bed and days when we couldn't wait to get to work, as it offered a sense of normalcy for us.

All of our systems were affected. Our minds, hearts, bodies, and spirits experienced and manifested deep anguish in their unique ways. Oddly, the initial pain paled in comparison to the pain felt in the wake of the loss. Indeed the pain of loss can arise when least expected and may continue to occur. In her poem "On Grief," May Sarton (1993) refers to some grief experiences being very loud while others are a whisper; some enduring, some transitory. There are as many expressions of grief as there are unique incidents and people on the planet.

Grief is often a misunderstood process in our culture. We are encouraged to move through it quickly. It can be considered an inconvenience to our "business as usual" schedule. People are often shocked, and sometimes even dismayed, when we still carry the grief of last month or last year. And yet, that is most common, even if it is not openly expressed. Grief is felt by every system of the self, even at the cellular level.

Honoring ourselves and the grief process is a type of self-care. We injure ourselves when we deny or suppress what we are experiencing. People around us may encourage us "to get over it" or "get on with life," and yet, this advice can feel inauthentic or even abrasive to us. We must hold reverence for our very unique process of grief, with all the arising emotional, mental and physical consequences, without any expectation of what it "should" look like. Others may not agree with or understand our process, and we must make peace with that. We must respect our own needs.

Grief arises with any loss. Changing jobs, ending a marriage, or getting a cancer diagnosis are all situations that may elicit grief. Even positive changes can bring grief as we mourn the loss of the old and familiar and step into the new and unknown. The presence of grief does not mean that we have made the wrong choice. This process is neither practical nor linear, and sometimes seems irrational. When we allow ourselves the complete experience of our emotions, they can become a source of richness and depth in self-knowledge.

Grief is a universal human response to the dance of life, to change and to letting go. It is to be honored and respected, not rushed through. *In response to our grief of losing Charly, our teacher Peggy reminded us that when we allow ourselves to be present with the tenderness and vulnerability of the heart breaking wide open, we are closer to the pulse of life and intimately connected with our bodhichitta – our awakened heart/mind.*

Grief cultivates wisdom and compassion when we look outside ourselves and connect with our brothers and sisters who have also suffered. An ancient mystical practice suggests that when we are feeling a difficult emotion, we bring to mind all of the people around the world who, in that moment, are sharing this same emotional experience. This connection to others in pain reminds us that our suffering is universal as well as personal.

Susan, a successful 45-year old banking executive, was a client who had been raped by her uncle when she was a teenager. She thought she had moved on with her life, and in many ways, she had. She got married, had children, and enjoyed a fulfilling, successful career. However, as she entered perimenopause, feelings of depression and anxiety began to surface. She had occasional panic attacks. She feared that the attacks would worsen to a debilitating level. She already had difficulty getting to work and focusing. After months of therapeutic work, Susan began to describe her story of sexual violation. She surprised herself with the intensity of emotions she felt and expressed.

Dr. Christiane Northrup's book The Wisdom of Menopause: Creating Physical and Emotional Health and Healing During the Change (2003) describes many similar situations, suggesting that as women move into menopause, old wounds begin to surface. This offers women an opportunity to heal at a deeper level. Susan worked with this information in therapy in a variety of ways including writing, talking, meditation and yoga, guided imagery, more writing and talking. She was guided to write letters and imagine-speak to her uncle (as if he were present in the room). This is a Gestalt technique in psychology called "empty chair," and many spiritual healers believe that when it is inappropriate to confront someone face-to-face, communicating spirit-to-spirit is highly effective.

Susan did some very deep and courageous work in many areas and yet, what helped her most significantly was an exercise of bringing to mind women around the world who also had been sexually violated. She imagined them in their various habitats and lifestyles, having a similar internal experience. She was able to connect to and empathize with their various feelings – shame, helplessness, anxiety, fear, betrayal, grief, and hopelessness. She was able to feel deep love for these women to whom she felt deeply connected. She wished for their healing as much as her own. Recognizing their connection, and the universality of suffering, helped Susan in the healing process.

The opening quote refers to the self as both human and spiritual. These two dimensions interplay throughout our lives, and especially in grief. In The Wise Heart: A Guide to the Universal Teachings of Buddhist Psychology (2008), Jack Kornfield writes, "A mature psychology requires us to see life from multiple perspectives." To understand loss from both a human and spiritual perspective provides a balm to ease our suffering. In Buddhist psychology, we recognize that we will all suffer in different ways, and that everything born will die, including all our friends and family members. This is both a personal truth and a universal reality.

We experience the personal pain of each loss, and we are universally connected by it as well. Honoring the personal experience of pain as well as its universality is key. The interplay of the two dimensions is what helps us move effectively and thoroughly through our grief, one minute, one day, or step at a time. Healing occurs when we understand ourselves and life through both the personal and universal, the human and spiritual, perspectives.

And while we may wish to avoid the experience of grief at all costs, when we allow the process to move through us, and ourselves to move through the process, an exquisite richness is woven into the tapestry of our lives.

Self-Reflection

What grief have you experienced in your life, big and small?

Do you have any unresolved grief that prevents you from living fully the gifts of your life?

Do you carry grief that needs to be revisited and worked on more deeply for healing?

Is there grief you are ready to release?

How can you understand your own experiences of loss through both the personal and universal perspectives? How might each lens help you heal?

Practice

Find a safe, quiet place to sit. Bring to a mind a situation that elicits grief. Notice the emotions that arise within you. Breathe into them, neither grasping nor rejecting them, just noticing. Find where the emotions are being held in the body. Bring your hands to that part of your body, as a symbol of warmth and tenderness. Allow yourself to feel the full range of emotions, riding the waves of each one into the next. If the emotions begin to dissipate, ask yourself if this is a time to release this grief. It may or may not be. You may release just a little. Use the exhale to let go of anything you would like to discharge. Notice the sensations in your body as you do so. Take some time at the end of this experience to just be. You may want to wrap yourself in a cozy blanket or enjoy a cup of tea. Return to this practice as often as you would like.

18

Forgiveness and Internal Knots

"If you harbor hatred or ill feelings toward a person, the feeling itself does not hurt the enemy. It only hurts your own peace of mind and eventually your health."
– *H. H. the Dalai Lama*

Exiled from his own country, and having witnessed the deaths of many innocents at the hands of the Chinese army, the Dalai Lama does not say these words lightly. He understands at a deep level what a lack of forgiveness can produce. If he can forgive his persecutors, certainly we, too, can move towards forgiveness. When Jesus hung on the cross, he prayed for his executioners, "Forgive them, Father, for they know not what they do." He was already practicing forgiveness, even as his tormenters brought him to death. Mahatma Gandhi, as he was assassinated, spoke words of forgiveness to his assassin. In all these examples, teachers advocated forgiveness, even in the midst of unimaginable pain. At the heart of any spiritual philosophy, you will find other teachers and mystics encouraging the same.

Often misunderstood in our culture, forgiveness does not imply that we agree with what happened, that we are willing to overlook what happened, or that we will allow it to happen again.

Sometimes, in order to forgive, we must put distance between ourselves and the persons we are forgiving. We tend to remain stuck in the familiarity of unforgiveness, afraid of being reinjured if we forgive, that we will lose the edge that we believe keeps us safe. We may think incorrectly of forgiveness as ignoring the injury, like it didn't happen or didn't matter. Consequently, we may retreat behind an emotional wall of resentment.

Forgiving does not mean putting ourselves in similar situations again. Instead, we relinquish the bondage that keeps us stuck and in pain. Self-righteousness is seductive. In forgiving, we lose the smugness and power of being right and the other person being wrong, but we gain freedom. In her book The Gift of Change: Spiritual Guidance for a Radically New Life (2006), Marianne Williamson encourages us to cultivate empathy for the offender because we cannot know their motivations. We might have done something similar or possibly worse given their circumstances and life experience.

Henry Wadsworth Longfellow wrote, "If we knew the secret history of our enemies, it would be enough to disarm all hostility." In mindfulness, we are reminded that there is much that does not meet the eye, so much occurring below the surface that we may never fully know. Wisdom and discernment lead us not only to look at the actions of another but also to consider the context in which those actions arose. Unforgiveness is like drinking a poison and expecting the other person to suffer. As the Dalai Lama mentions in the opening quote, it harms us on many levels.

In another of her books, Return to Love: Reflections on the Principles of "A Course in Miracles," (1996), Marianne Williamson compares having an attack thought about another to dropping a sword on one's own head, and yet the ego seduces us towards blame or finding faults in others. The ego is tenacious in its quest to assign blame. Our true nature wishes to be free from this bondage.

Everett Worthington Jr., a psychology professor at Virginia Commonwealth University, who became a pioneer in forgiveness research, has substantiated the deleterious effects of unforgiveness and the benefits of forgiveness. In Forgiveness and Reconciliation: Theory and Application (2006), Dr. Worthington chronicles the healing power of forgiveness in couples, families and individuals.

Science Daily (January 2008) reported a study by the Mayo Clinic on the harmful health effects surrounding unforgiveness. The study showed that holding a grudge appears to affect the cardiovascular and nervous systems. People who focused on a personal grudge had elevated blood pressure and heart rates, as well as increased muscle tension and feelings of being less in control. Conversely, when participants were asked to imagine forgiving a person who had hurt them, the physiological measures improved.

Forgiveness is most often a process. Occasionally, we decide to forgive and experience an immediate sense of completion, but that is rare. Mostly, we must return to the process, forgiving a bit more each time. Frequently, we think we've forgiven certain people, then resentment resurfaces. Clients sometimes feel frustrated, believing that the work they did previously was futile. We remind them that their earlier work paved the way for the profound work they are now ready and willing to do. Each time we return to the process of forgiveness, we work at a deeper level until the process feels complete.

Forgiveness requires courage and a willingness to let go. It calls for inner strength and equanimity, and most of all, self-love. We forgive, not for the other person, but for ourselves. Because we love ourselves enough, we choose not to carry this heaviness, this poison in our minds, heart, bodies, and spirits. Through forgiveness, we find greater joy, compassion, freedom, spaciousness, and equanimity.

Forgiveness of self is a practice often postponed. This is because it requires deep emotional excavation. As we move through this process, we discover painful internal injuries. These inner knots frequently manifest as guilt, shame, and regret, and can lead to behavioral and relational problems. Diligence and compassion are essential to gently and carefully untying these knots, thread by thread.

Derek carried an internal knot of regret that permeated his life. He abused alcohol and sabotaged relationships. He was a workaholic whose perpetual anxiety impeded any type of true relaxation, even on weekends or during vacations. When Derek was nineteen years old, two significant events occurred. His mother was diagnosed with Parkinson's Disease, and as her condition deteriorated, she needed assistance at home. He refused to give up his life to help her. Instead, his younger sister dropped out of college to care for her. After their mother died, his sister fell into a deep depression and never returned to school. She struggled to make ends meet.

Also during this time, Derek impregnated his girlfriend, and they chose to have an abortion. At age 41, regret, guilt, and shame saturated Derek's being. The bottomless pain of the past prevented him from living fully. At the deepest level, he felt unworthy of a fulfilling life because of the choices he made as a young man, and subconsciously he was determined to punish himself. Derek reluctantly came to counseling due to a DUI charge. We began addressing his alcohol abuse and eventually uncovered the internal turmoil driving his dysfunctional behaviors. With courage and care, he began untying the knots that bound him to feelings of worthlessness. He asked forgiveness of his sister, his girlfriend, and his mother. Most importantly, he forgave himself. He learned to practice acceptance (the willingness to see things clearly) and true compassion for himself and others.

We all have made mistakes in our lives, and we all will make mistakes in our future. We will cause harm despite our intentions, and may not even realize it. Remembering this can help us when we judge others harshly. Extending mercy to ourselves and others is a central principle of living compassionately and peacefully. Phillip Moffit, author of Dancing with Life: Buddhist Insights for Finding Meaning and Joy in the Face of Suffering (2007), reminds us that redemption is possible for everyone. There is a reason we go in droves to movies which have a theme of redemption. They touch our humanity, open our hearts, and give us the hope that we, too, can be redeemed from past mistakes.

As human beings, we do and say things that cause harm, knowingly or unknowingly. Others do the same. As a practice, we can ask for forgiveness, person-to-person or spirit-to-spirit. In 12-step programs, this process is called making amends. Sometimes, it is not possible or best to do this person-to-person. In the book and movie Eat Pray Love: One Woman's Search for Everything for Everything Across Italy, India and Indonesia (2007), Elizabeth Gilbert connects spirit-to-spirit with her ex-husband, asking forgiveness for any harm she caused him. We each can offer and ask forgiveness for anything we are ready to release. Personal work of untying our internal knots must coincide with any abiding forgiveness offer or request. Many people fool themselves by thinking they can simply say they have forgiven and the process is over. The personal work of forgiveness requires us to face our pain. This can be so difficult that we are tempted to deny the impact a person or situation has had on us.

Finally, offer forgiveness to yourself for any mistakes you have made - for any ways you have harmed yourself or others, knowingly or unknowingly. As you practice, bring your hand to your heart, offer yourself unconditional love and acceptance, see the innocence within, and extend mercy. As the Indian master Bapuji echoes "And breathe---into the goodness that you are."

Self-Reflection

In what ways are you stuck in unforgiveness, of yourself or others?

What internal knots would you like to untie – mental, emotional, physical, spiritual?

What are the consequences of unforgiveness in your life? (Most are easily detected in behaviors and relationships.)

Practice

Make a forgiveness list – those you are willing to forgive, those from whom you would ask forgiveness, and ways in which you would like to forgive yourself. Create a safe, quiet space where you will not be disturbed, and begin to work through your list. You may want to use ritual by lighting a candle or incense, wrapping yourself in a meditation or prayer shawl, etc. As a symbolic gesture of releasing, you may want to write the forgiveness list and tear it up, burn it, flush it, etc. You may want to speak directly to some on your list. It may be helpful to write your thoughts and feelings before you have these conversations. Remember that these encounters should cause no further harm to you or other persons.

19

Generosity

"For it is in giving that we receive."
-St. Francis of Assisi

Generosity is one of the paramitas (or principles) of mindful living. The Sanskrit word for generosity is dana. Generosity is a part of the heart-opening practice that allows love and goodness to flow through our lives. We can practice generosity in many ways. Obviously, with material things, we can give money or gifts. We can offer our time to others, in service work or sitting down to listen. We can be generous with our talents by helping with a project or imparting our wisdom. We can be generous with our attention by talking less and allowing others to talk more or by relinquishing the spotlight so that others have an opportunity to be heard and seen. We can extend positive comments of support and encouragement. We can be generous in our assessments of others and the world. We can participate in random acts of kindness.

Karma yoga is the form of yoga dedicated to "selfless service." We believe that service work is a key component of psychological wellness and spiritual development, both personally and for the well-being of the world. The ever-present mystical teaching "We are all one" reminds us that as we help others, we benefit as well.

Remembering our interconnectedness restores something deep within the psyche and the heart. We are truly in this together, even in the midst of feeling alienated or lonely.

Patanjali, who compiled the *Yoga Sutras* about 2500 years ago, described avidya, a human condition of ignorance whereby ego separates us from others and our true spiritual nature. Vidya, on the other hand, is knowledge, a powerful knowledge of non-separation, non-duality. When we are generous, we are living in vidya. And when we live in vidya, we are at peace.

For depressed or anxious clients, we may recommend engaging in service work of some type. When we help others, we often feel better, knowing that we have something to offer. Everyone has something to offer. We have a friend who was recently unemployed and has little money. Many people in his position would say that they have nothing to give. Yet, he volunteers with several organizations that are meaningful to him, and he finds that he feels better as a result. Volunteering does not create money or a new job for him, but the sense of self-efficacy and of helping creates a richness within that would elude him if he focused only on earning money and finding a new job.

In the book, The Power of Doing Good (2001), authors Allan Luks and Peggy Payne describe the effects of helping or serving others as akin to the experience of a hardy workout. Initially, a person feels a sense of exhilaration and energy called "the helper's high" followed by a feeling of calm and serenity. In 1998, Luks, the Executive Director of Big Brothers, Big Sisters in New York City, first described this "helper's high," which results from the release of a potent mixture of serotonin, dopamine, and other neurochemicals. These chemicals act to increase our heartbeats, bring tears to our eyes, and give us that warm-glow feeling.

Random acts of kindness are a particularly powerful way to practice generosity. The movie Pay it Forward (2000) illustrates how each of us can make a difference in the lives of others. In this movie, a twelve-year old boy creates a plan to do something kind for another and, in return, asks only that the receiver "pay it forward." This child has faith in the inherent goodness of everyone and sets out to prove it. The audience follows the ripple effect of kindness through the lives of seemingly unconnected characters. The chain of events reveals that we are connected at the deepest level of our humanity. We all want to be seen, cared about, and treated with kindness.

A 2008 study by researchers James Fowler (University of California, San Diego) and Nicholas Christakis (Harvard University) suggests that cooperative behavior spreads between people. When a person receives kindness, s/he is more likely to extend kindness to others. These researchers reinforce the idea of generosity contagion.

Studies show that being a part of an act of kindness raises the serotonin levels in the brain whether you are the giver, the receiver, or even a witness to the act. A study at Harvard, dubbed "The Mother Teresa Effect," showed that the saliva levels of Immunoglobin A (a critical antibody in the immune system) were raised after observing a film about Mother Teresa's work among the poor of Calcutta.

We can all be creative in our acts of kindness. *We (Angela and Dennis) enjoy paying the toll for the car behind us, handing out umbrellas to those who forgot when it's raining, or giving out water in the hot Atlanta summers to those waiting at the bus stop. We, the givers, experience as much joy in these experiences as the recipients.*

In other supporting studies of generosity, authors Stephen Post, Ph.D. and Jill Neimark, Ph.D. (Why Good Things Happen To Good People, 2007) validate the psychological and physical benefits of volunteerism and philanthropy, for both the giver and the receiver. One of the results is a longer life. Studies at UC Berkeley and UT Austin have also substantiated this, specifically regarding life extension.

We all have different patterns when it comes to generosity. Some of us refrain or withhold while others overextend. We give so much that there is nothing left for us. This is when we become codependent, giving to our own detriment. We must ask ourselves whether our giving is in balance. If it produces resentment, we may have gone too far.

Giving with expectation can also present problems. "Clean" generosity is giving without expecting reciprocity or even a thank you. We extend ourselves because we choose to extend, whatever the results. Clean generosity is extending and then letting go. Even more powerful is giving without taking credit for the act of service. This removes the ego altogether which always wants to be fed, and feeding the ego does very little for the growth of the essential spirit within. Conversely, true generosity fosters a strong, inner core, a calmness and peace at the deepest levels.

Being on the **receiving** end of generosity can make us feel vulnerable. Some clients explain that they feel uncomfortable when being helped because it makes them feel "less than" or "helpless" and sometimes "unworthy" of receiving. It can also feel very intimate. In some cultures, giving is considered a great privilege. Groups vie to bring dinner to a family in need or to participants in a retreat. They have wisdom about the joy and merit of giving and helping.

When you block someone from giving to you, you do him or her great disservice. You block his or her experience of generosity. Receiving graciously from others is another form of generosity. If you have a pattern of overextending and not receiving, take some time to explore this. What would it be like to do things differently?

We train people how to treat us. If we are constantly in the "helping" role, we may appear needless and wantless. Yet, we all have needs and desires. It's important to our health to acknowledge and honor these. Perhaps if your pattern is one of always helping and rarely receiving, it could be beneficial to voice your feelings and needs more often. Priscilla, a wise woman in our Cancer Wellness sangha, is a wonderful model for voicing needs directly. She does this unapologetically, with a combination of directness and kindness.

Since it may initially feel awkward, we suggest experimenting with emotionally safe individuals first, then working your way toward those who may be more difficult. As you commit to honoring yourself daily, this will become more and more natural for you. Balance, even in generosity practice, is skillful.

Self-Reflection

What are your personal patterns with generosity?

Have you ever thought about being generous but chose to withhold? Have you had an impulse to be generous and followed through without analyzing it? How did each of these experiences make you feel within?

Do you have a pattern of being overly generous? Or blocking generosity when it's offered to you?

Do you tend to give only in certain ways? How can you offer generosity through different means?

Practice

Try practicing generosity in a new way. For example, if you express generosity through gifts or money, try listening more or extending patience or a smile. If your generosity practice most often revolves around extending warmth to others, try offering something more tangible. Notice what it feels like to broaden your generosity toolbox, and extend in ways that are different. Have fun, be creative, and enjoy yourself!

20

Right Effort

"Being mindful is not difficult. But it's difficult to be continuously aware. For that you need right effort."
- Sayadaw U Tejaniya

In Buddhist psychology, right effort is taught as a part of the Four Noble Truths and Eight-fold path. *Whenever we discuss this topic in workshops, it generates a lot of energy and dialogue.* Right effort is taught as practicing due diligence, knowing when to hold on and when to let go. It can also be described as the middle way, the balance between doing and being. Practicing right effort offers opportunities for deeper psychological and emotional understanding.

In Western culture, we grow up believing that our accomplishments are our identity. Beneath that belief is a chronic hum of "not enough," so that we become driven and overstimulated. One student referred to this experience as a large, black, ominous dog chasing her. If she doesn't keep moving, she fears that something horrible will happen. When she awakens in the early morning hours, she reviews her "to do" list to ensure that nothing fell through the cracks. When we met in yoga class, she was suffering from chronic fatigue syndrome and other auto-immune disorders. She feared that her life was about to fall apart, and in a way it did.

It also opened the possibility of a whole new way of being for her.

Different phases of our lives call for different paces. When we have a goal, it may be wise to take more action. This requires focus and attention. We sometimes see clients who have goals but are unwilling to do the work these goals require. They would rather just dream about and talk about their goals. They are too laid back or lackadaisical. Manifesting our ideas and dreams requires a push, temporary sacrifice, and what is called "heroic effort." *In writing this book, we (Angela and Dennis) have often put social engagements and creative work projects on the back burner. Once the book is completed, it will be imperative for us to return to more balance out of self-care, right effort, and wise action.* Wise action arises from right effort. Problems appear when we continue in this vein of doing, never returning to a place of right effort and balance. Becoming addicted to the rush of "doing" and accomplishment is possible. The idea of achieving goal after goal can be a seductive force, guiding us toward "workaholism" and eventual disease.

We live in a world of addictions. Some are blatant, like alcohol and drug addiction. Others are more subtle, like addiction to food, sex, money, accomplishment, recognition, television, noise, people, or simply getting what we want, when we want it, the way we want it. To test your own tendency towards this pattern, try having a cup of coffee or tea every morning for a month. On the thirty-first day, do not allow yourself to have the drink, then notice what arises.

Addiction to a fast pace of life, especially in the technology age, is common. We have a strong attachment to speed – with emails, texts, etc. Notice what arises in you when your computer stalls for a few seconds. This sense of urgency and attachment to immediate results manifests more strongly in our lives when we are not practicing right effort.

There are times in our lives that call for less doing and more being. For example, drastic life changes such as receiving a cancer diagnosis or losing a loved one require us to slow down and let go. This can feel uncomfortable for many. So often we want to continue working as hard as before, to continue doing and accomplishing. Innocently, but unskillfully, people around us may try to reinforce "business as usual" because they are unsure of how to help. Changes in us may also be uncomfortable for them. They may react in various ways to the slowing down process - with disappointment, confusion, or even non-acceptance. They may feel threatened or uneasy.

Often cancer patients feel the need to take care of their loved ones' emotions before their own. This is the time when they must trust themselves and the organic pacing determined from within. This is the time to let go of second-guessing and practice acceptance, allowing all the emotional, physical, mental, spiritual, behavioral, and relational changes to be what they are.

In the classic serenity prayer, one line wisely advises us to "… accept the things we cannot change." Acceptance, wisdom, and clarity are key components of right effort. Understanding and respecting the rhythm that is right for you in different phases of your life leads you to skillful behavior. Only you can determine this for yourself.

We observe our yoga and meditation students struggling with right effort. Some students do not put forth the effort required to gain traction or reap benefits from their practice. Others may become too rigid and ego-driven, suffering greatly when the components are not in place for the "perfect" practice session. Some try only those poses that are easy for them, not wanting to attempt new poses in which they may feel awkward or "less than." Others push too hard, injuring themselves or reinforcing the ego wounding of "better than." Right effort guides us to hold ourselves, our lives and our practices with an attitude of "not too tight and not too loose," noticing when it is right for us to forge ahead and when it is time to accept, rest, and restore.

Self-Reflection

How has right effort played out in your life? Where do you find yourself challenged? Do you have a tendency toward overdoing or not doing enough?

Can you remember times when you leaned toward doing when slowing down or letting go would have been more appropriate and beneficial? Or the reverse?

Can you identify the underlying reasons for your patterns?

What insights have you gained along the way? What lessons have you learned?

Practice

Choose a day to alter your patterns of doing/being. Notice how a different pacing feels to you. Practice a mixture of activity, slowing down, and letting go. Notice your thoughts, emotions, and bodily sensations.

21

Mindful Consumption

"Our work is not to change what you do, but to witness what you do with enough awareness, enough curiosity, enough tenderness that the lies and old decisions upon which the compulsion is based become apparent and fall away."
- *Geneen Roth*

When we consider consumption, we may first think of food. Mindful eating, an integral part of mindful practice, is discussed in more depth in the Practices section at the end of this book. Mindful consumption is an even broader topic that refers to anything we take in - television, news, music, conversation, gossip, emails, medicines, drugs, advertisements, ideas, etc. We are constantly consuming something, sometimes consciously and sometimes not.

In practicing mindful consumption, we increase awareness of what we take in and why. For example, if you watch disturbing television programs on a regular basis, you imprint your psyche with fear-based content. If you do this regularly, you may think that it does not affect you. We often suggest to clients a week-long diet from fear-based programming. When clients do this, we often see dramatic reductions in their levels of anxiety, fear, and stress. Notice how you feel before bed when you watch something funny or light instead of something disturbing. You will probably notice a positive difference in your sense of well-being and your quality of sleep.

Mindful consumption also refers to conversations, verbal as well as electronic. If we participate in unkind jokes, gossip, or other negativity, we harm ourselves and others. Cultivating wholesome seeds within ourselves allows calm, compassion, and clarity. When we consciously or unconsciously allow our minds to become cluttered with harmful sentiments, we block the unfolding of our own greater good.

We can extend this approach to anything we consume. *In our work at Cancer Wellness at Piedmont Hospital, we encourage patients to consider this when receiving radiation and chemotherapy treatments.* Often grueling, these treatments are used for healing. When something is painful to us, we often react by recoiling. With mindful consumption of medications or treatments, it is helpful to change our negative mindset and create a conscious intention of healing. Some patients even create a mantra or prayer to pair with treatment, affirming their intention to heal.

When evaluating your own mindful consumption practices, consider your motivations. Why do you choose to consume certain things? What drives the consumption? Why do you reach for more?

Michael started each day with the morning news, as many Americans do. He felt deprived if he missed it. He thought this information would allow him to control life more. As we explored the concept of control, Michael realized that much of his personal life was out of control. He was not attending to areas that needed his attention, specifically his problems with anxiety. When he tried the news diet for a week, he initially felt extremely uncomfortable. As he continued the diet, his anxiety decreased. He felt more centered and stable each day, not as uptight and agitated. He could stay informed by listening, reading, and watching the news less often, and, without the negative distraction, he could address other issues.

Carol gained 30 pounds in the past two years from mindless eating. When she kept a food journal for a couple of weeks, she discovered that she was eating "just a little more" at each sitting; nibbling on chips as she prepared dinner, having an extra cookie, or an additional glass of wine. Once Carol identified the behaviors, she began to explore underlying emotions. She was grieving over her mom's death, and she felt ongoing pressure with her work. Once she allowed herself to experience and express her full range of emotions, she slowly resumed healthy and mindful consumption.

As with any consumption, types of music consumed can also have either a positive or negative effect on our health. The research of Dr. David Hawkins, in Power vs. Force: The Hidden Determinants of Human Behavior (2002), reviews music's effects at the molecular level. Rap music, for example, is considered harmful. Also, any type of music exceeding a certain decibel level creates a stress response in the body.

When we address the underlying motivations for our habitual consumption behaviors, solid progress begins. We miss a wealth of wisdom and healing when we focus solely on the behaviors themselves. As Geneen Roth suggests in the opening quote, we must proceed with awareness, curiosity, and tenderness towards ourselves.

Self-Reflection

Evaluate your own consumption patterns – positive and negative. Consider television, magazines, books, goods, advertising, conversations, internet sites and blogs, music, medicine, medical treatments, spiritual messages, food and drink, cigarettes, caffeine, drugs, art, teachings, and ideas. Write about these patterns once a week.

What might be motivating your unskillful or non-mindful consumption? You may not know readily so take some time to brainstorm. Perhaps use the sentence stem, "I may be consuming this because…"
or "The feelings I notice when I do not consume this are…."

Where have you seen progress with mindful consumption practices?

Practice

Choose a day to practice mindful consumption. You may want to focus on one area or include several areas. Notice your thoughts, feelings, internal dialogue, and behaviors. Note any internal and external experiences.

22

Humor and Mindfulness

"A person without a sense of humor is like a wagon without springs. It's jolted by every pebble on the road."
-Henry Ward Beecher

Have you ever seen a statue of the laughing Buddha? That image doesn't suggest that life unfolds as an endless, austere series of tragedies, does it? Buddhist teachings do recognize life's pain, but the degree to which we suffer depends on us. Norman Fischer suggests that "to laugh in the midst of your own suffering is to respond to the divine comedy of the human condition." Mindfulness reminds us to take ourselves lightly, that it is skillful to cultivate joy. Humor, and its behavioral outlet, laughter, reduce our suffering. Laughter enables us to feel good.

Recall a time when you laughed heartily, perhaps at the actions of a friend. You may remember feeling bathed in warm, pleasant feelings within minutes of the experience. Those feelings are caused by the activation of endorphins in the body. When we laugh, we stimulate the release of pain-reducing hormones in the brain. Moments later, we feel better.

Research shows the extensive benefits of humor, particularly when it leads to laughter. In a study by Lee S. Berk, M.P.H., Dr.P.H., David L. Felten, M.D., et al. (2001), researchers concluded that "modulation of neuroimmune parameters during and following the humor-associated eustress of laughter may provide beneficial health effects for wellness and a complementary adjunct to whole-person integrative medicine therapies." Other studies document that humor and laughter specifically benefit us by stimulating production of t-lymphocyte cells (enhanced immune system), increasing production of serotonin (a "feel good" neurotransmitter), producing flexibility in the joints and muscles, improving circulation (massaging organs), and resulting in a better mood/disposition.

In a 2003 study, Dr. Mary Bennett, et al., at Western Kentucky University, found that humor produces increased immune function and concluded that laughter boosts natural killer cell (NK) activity. For anyone, particularly those with immune-compromised disease, laughter proves invaluable.

A recent article in Buddhadharma (Summer 2011) by a comedic actress and Buddhist practitioner, Elaine Smookler, hit the nail on the head when she commented that "Nothing is more ridiculous than our sense of self-importance, so why not welcome opportunities to see the buffoon in us all?" Taking ourselves more lightly is central to the mindful path and leads to more peace and happiness.

Studies indicate that adults laugh about five times a day whereas children laugh about 35-40 times daily. And infants laugh about 400 times each day! By the time we reach adulthood, the frequency of laughter reaches its lowest point. After all, we believe that life is serious, and humor is silly and non-productive. Allowing ourselves to return to the spontaneous, uninhibited laughter of childhood helps keep life in perspective.

Humor produces panoramic awareness. When you laugh at life's absurdity, you enter the present moment fully. When you laugh, you create a feeling of spaciousness and a sense of openness. This facilitates better problem-solving and a renewed perspective. Like meditation, laughter allows us to let go.

For Dennis, laughter is the great equalizer. And no one makes him laugh harder than Angela. Frequently, it's her quick wit, the way she affectionately jokes with him, and best of all, her humorous, spontaneous dances or silly voices that cause him to erupt in laughter. Within minutes of her amusing actions, Dennis enjoys a deep sense of relaxation and a renewed, more balanced perspective.

In Dennis' humor workshops with cancer patients, participants recollect humorous events surrounding their experiences with diagnosis, treatment, medical staff, family and friends. Some have even written entire books on their experiences. Finding the lighter side of an otherwise grim medical concern allows patients to feel better and to gain a more positive perspective.

In relationship counseling and coaching, we observe couples who become so stubborn about their own stances that a contempt process develops, and the love in their relationship is lost. They decide to be right instead of happy. When couples become accountable for their actions while also laughing at themselves, they can make significant shifts and lasting differences.

When we catch ourselves hooked by monkey mind or ego, we can choose to laugh at ourselves. We can choose to smile at our humanity and breathe into the space that humor creates. Humor is good medicine – for the mind, heart, body, and spirit.

We would like to end this chapter with some counselor humor:
How many therapists does it take to change a light bulb?
One, but the light bulb has to be <u>willing</u> to change…

Self-Reflection

What activities encourage you to laugh? (comedy, sitcoms, cartoons, joke books, etc.)

Which funny people can you associate with more frequently?

Write down the name of at least one person who truly tickles your funny bone. ________________ What does this person do that makes you laugh?

What is a difficult or complex situation in which you can use humor?

Practice

Give yourself permission to find humor in your daily affairs. Look at your current difficulties through the filter of humor.

Laugh often, and notice the shifts that take place in yourself and others.

When you are feeling down, retrieve a memory of laughing really hard. Allow your mind to guide you into the memory as if it is happening now. Remember, the brain doesn't know the difference between what is real or imagined, so you will reap the same benefits and feel better in the process.

23

Spirituality

"My religion is kindness."
- H.H. the Dalai Lama

We (Angela and Dennis) teach mindfulness through the door of psychology, and we personally incorporate it into our own spiritual practices. Not aligned with any particular organized religious system, spirituality is central to our lives and guides us daily. We find great value in many teachings: Buddhist, Christian, Native American, Celtic, Religious Science, Taoism, A Course in Miracles, Poetry of Rumi, Hafiz, Mary Oliver, and others. Our students come from various spiritual paths, some very specific and organized, and some more eclectic in nature. We honor each person's choice. We find that mindfulness teachings are not contrary to any spiritual path and, in fact, align with the true essence of nearly all paths.

Regardless of what you call it, many of us recognize an energy beyond the physical. Some refer to this energy as the big "I AM." Many call this connective life force God or Spirit. Some use words like Infinite Love, Nature, the All that Is, Brahman, Atman, Jesus, the Ultimate Dimension, Our True Nature, Compassionate Presence, Christ Consciousness, Buddha Nature, the Tao, Allah, Pure Awareness, Divine Intelligence, and The Universe. What we call this mystical presence is unimportant. That we access it and let it guide us is essential.

An old minister of ours, Dr. Kennedy Schultz of the Atlanta Spiritual Living Center in Atlanta, used to say that "what you are looking for is what you are looking with." As Ramana Maharshi reminds us, "It is always, already here," within us and all around us. Jesus said, "The kingdom of heaven is within you." You can find this spiritual presence in all things everywhere, and you can find it in yourself. Our experience as human beings is similar to the wave in the ocean; we each manifest in our unique expressions, but we are always a part of the greater whole. As Sri Ramkrishna reminds us, "The winds of grace are always blowing, but you must raise your sail."

A fish swimming in the ocean looking for water is similar to humans searching for Spirit. Spirit is around us and within us all the time. When we slow our frantic pace, practicing stillness and quiet, we get a glimpse of this truth. With more practice, this glimpse becomes a window of light. The more time and energy we invest in connecting with Pure Awareness, the more it permeates our lives.

Many traditions encourage meditation as a way to hear "the still, small voice within." At a harried pace, we run quickly through the stream of life and cannot understand why the water is so cloudy. As we stop, becoming still and quiet, particles settle to the bottom of the stream and clarity manifests. We receive answers; we discern solutions; and we discover a deeper wisdom.

Perhaps you have had an experience of "synchronicity" in which seemingly unrelated events became connected and could not be coincidental - when you have felt that something larger was speaking to you. In spiritual schools of thought, synchronicity is considered a result of Spirit connecting all things, in divine right timing and order.

Calvin thought it "odd" and "a weird, freaky thing" that weeks after he lost his 25 year-old son in a tragic motorcycle accident, he crossed paths with his high school sweetheart, who also lost her son in an accident. Coincidence? As Calvin and his sweetheart discussed the circumstances, they discovered both sons were killed in separate cities *on the same night.* Calvin had been thinking of Lucinda, and while passing through Atlanta on her way home, *she* thought about giving him a call. Each was divorced, and both had considered marrying the other at one time. Their "chance" meeting occurred at a fast food restaurant where Calvin had never eaten. Lucinda rarely eats fast food. And yes, this story has a happy ending complete with an old love rekindled and an unimagined, sweet connection.

Synchronicity, the presence of Spirit connecting all things, increases as we recognize and validate it. When we are open and receptive to its presence in our lives, our steps become lighter, and we move through the world with more ease and grace. Spiritual presence goes before us and paves the way.

In some support groups, the word "ego" is used as an acronym for "Edging God Out." The more we allow ourselves to rest in Spirit, to have faith that a higher force is present, the more we transform. Ego-based fear is replaced with peace and love, and many of our "problems" dissolve. The way you define God, a higher power, a loving energy, is your choice. As counselors and coaches, we have observed distinct differences between those who approach life spiritually and those who don't.

The practices at the end of the book can become a part of your own spiritual practice if you wish. They can also facilitate psychological development. In whatever way you choose to use them, they will assist you in cultivating the four C's - calm, compassion, clarity, and choice – in your life. As Hafiz expresses, "We have come into this exquisite world to experience ever and ever more deeply our divine courage, freedom, and light."

Self-Reflection

In what ways can you pause in the stream of life?

How much time are you willing to commit to quiet contemplation?

What helps you feel connected? (people, activities, teachers)

What spiritual traditions or practices appeal to you? Which new practices would you like to incorporate into your current practices?

What ideas or rituals have been helpful in the past?

Practice

Explore new rituals or practices in your spiritual tradition, or explore practices from a spiritual tradition different from your own.

Try to refrain from judgment, examining other traditions for their value and merit.

24

The Way of the Bodhisattva

"Glimpses of the Bodhi mind are powerful. By nurturing these states of mind, they grow larger in our experience. It lifts us out of self-centeredness and gives us a chance to leave dysfunctional habits behind."

–Pema Chodron

Bodhi, the root of the word bodhisattva, refers to the tree under which the Buddha attained enlightenment. Bodhisattva refers to those who are on the mindful path, committed to nurturing qualities of compassion and wisdom within themselves. Bodhisattvas are committed to waking up, becoming more conscious, and helping others do the same. Everyone has this potential within them. We all have the seed of goodness within called the bodhichitta – "the awakened heart/mind." If we choose to water this seed of goodness through mindful living, it will grow larger.

We each have the potential to be a force for good in this world. As we commit to this path through regular practice of mindful yoga and meditation, as well as opening and growing around the insights we gain about ourselves, we return to our true nature - love. Abiding in love, we move through the world as a healing light, bringing a sense of well-being, not only to ourselves and our loved ones, but to all we encounter. The root word for bodhisattva in English is bud, symbolizing blossoming or awakening. The famous Christian story of Saint Francis of Assisi, who just by his pure essence attracted the company of various animals, is one of a bodhisattva. The prayer of Saint Francis resounds with the Bodhisattva code:

Lord, make me an instrument of Thy peace;
Where there is hatred, let me sow love;
Where there is injury, pardon;
Where there is error, truth;
Where there is doubt, faith;
Where there is despair, hope;
Where there is darkness, light;
And where there is sadness, joy.

O Divine Master,
Grant that I may not so much seek
To be consoled, as to console;
To be understood, as to understand;
To be loved as to love.

For it is in giving that we receive;
It is in pardoning that we are pardoned;
And it is in dying that we are born to eternal life.

Remember that perfection isn't necessary to nurture the bodhichitta within. Bodhisattvas simply aspire to live with an awakened heart and mind. Boddhisattvas are committed to cutting through their own self-deception. In his poem "You Are Me," Thich Nhat Hanh echoes this: "I transform the garbage in myself, so that you do not have to suffer." Working on ourselves is a part of the bodhisattva path.

As Pema suggests in the introductory quote, even a glimpse of our own boddhi mind can be very powerful and compelling. When we return to that place, our hearts are open, our minds are clear, and we feel a sense of equanimity, of being grounded and calm. The brahma viharas – loving-kindness, compassion, joy, and equanimity - provide a clear compass for returning to this place, again and again. Meditation, yoga, chanting, and mindful walking are some of the tools of the bodhisattva.

The "paramitas" provide a guide for nurturing and growing our bodhichitta . The word paramita is Sanskrit for "gone to the other shore," meaning the ability to let go and practice living in the impermanence of life with a sense of internal steadiness. Various teachers discuss the paramitas in different ways. Some teachers refer to six paramitas, and others refer to ten. These are not commandments but rather guides to optimal well-being and awakening. We each find our own way with them. We've listed the paramitas below with a brief and simple description of each:

1 – Generosity – giving of oneself, without attachment

2 – Discipline – self-discipline, maintaining focus on path

3 – Patience – opening and softening, not pushing and controlling

4 – Joyful Exertion – practicing right effort with an open heart

5 – Meditation – formal and informal, mindful on the mat and in life

6 – Wisdom – clarity, self-knowledge, releasing delusion

An additional four paramitas have been added (based on the attainment of the first six).

7 – Skillful Means – using our resources for a higher good

8 – Spiritual Aspirations – noble intention, beyond self-focus

9 – Higher Accomplishments – helping others, relieving suffering

10 – Awakened Awareness – complete enlightenment, always abiding in the realm of the Divine, permanent recognition of "no separation"

Teachers have written entire books dedicated to the paramitas. To learn more about these, see the resources at the end of this book.

Bodhisattvas are considered spiritual warriors, warriors committed to growing in self-awareness, to waking up. Bodhisattvas learn to relieve their own suffering by cutting through their own habitual reactionary patterns, and then help others do the same by shining their own bright lights. They have made a commitment to serve others. This does not mean they have chosen a vocation that is dedicated to service. In fact, any vocation can be a ministry of mindfulness. Rather, it is the way they do business, the way they do life, that is their path of service to others.

There are many modern-day bodhisattvas. Oprah Winfrey is perhaps one of them. There are visible ones and invisible ones. *We (Angela and Dennis) met Bill on a trip to Asheville. At first glance, one may not recognize him as a modern-day bodhisattva. He is a local plumber who looks rather scruffy and has a gruff tenor in his voice. We sat next to him at the deli counter of a local restaurant, exchanged a few words about the weather and the town, and then Bill left. After he left, the owners of this restaurant filled us in on who Bill really is. He works as a plumber, fixing not only the pipes of his paying customers but also offering his services free of charge on the weekends (his off days) to those who cannot afford him, particularly the elderly and the disabled.* Bill makes a decent living as a plumber but is not wealthy by any means. However, he still finds a way to contribute regularly and substantially to several local non-profit organizations that are in need of help. Bill is a modern day bodhisattva, who has awakened to his inner calling of serving others.

Many things can hide our bodhichitta...the busyness of life, our absorption in our own problems, and the three roots of suffering – grasping, aversion, and delusion. Grasping can keep us focused on the next best thing for ourselves - always wanting more and better, reinforcing our "all-caught-up-ness" in ME. Aversion can cause us to make negative snap judgments about people, situations, possibilities, and our own abilities to help. Delusion can block us from seeing ourselves and others clearly, from witnessing both the beauty and the suffering happening around us, and from hearing the internal call, the bodhichitta, that seeks to alleviate pain.

As we mature emotionally and spiritually, we begin to settle down and turn our attention inward. We remember our true nature, the divine essence that is central to our being. We recognize the inherent goodness in ourselves, and if we stay on the path of mindfulness, nurturing the seeds of bodhichitta, we learn to live day-to-day from this powerful and steadfast place, with an open heart and a wise mind. The addiction to ME and the three roots of suffering becomes less compelling and less rewarding. We become more fearless, able to love ourselves and all of life around us, with ease and grace.

Self-Reflection

Do you have an armoring of defensiveness or self-protectiveness around the tenderness of your heart?

In what ways does this armoring cover your bodhichitta?

How can you nourish the bodhisattva in you, the seeds of goodness and personal power?

How would you like to help others and be a force for good in the world? In what ways are you already doing this?

Practice

See yourself as a bodhisattva – the spiritual warrior – that you are. Choose a day to allow this part of you to take the lead – in how you think, talk, and behave. Note any observations or insights.

25

We're All In This Together

"The sangha boat is a place where you can lay your oars down and allow others to row for you."
–Peggy Rowe-Ward and Larry Ward

As you begin your journey of mindful living, remember that we are all in this together. You are not alone. Even those you consider to be more advanced in this teaching are also on the path. Once you embark on the journey of living mindfully, you may feel worse before you feel better as you become more conscious about parts of you that you may not like or value. People say in the first year of this practice that they had not realized many of their flaws until now. In truth, those demons run our lives from a subconscious or unconscious control room until we have the courage to bring those parts of ourselves into the conscious light. Then, we have the chance to heal and transform ourselves through the alchemy of mindful living.

Fortunately, we do not have to do this perfectly. The reality is we will not do this perfectly. Sometimes this is the expectation when people begin this path, that they will go from grace to grace, in a linear progression to perfection. We won't always hit our mark. No one does. The truth is that you (and we) will likely take one step forward and two steps back as we make progress. Patience and mercy are required. The teachings remind us that we can start over at any point. If we are in the middle of an anger tantrum or a judgmental attack thought, we can catch ourselves in that moment and choose to start again. Or it may be in hindsight, after the tantrum or thought, that we realize we veered off the path. At that moment of realization, we can re-commit ourselves. We can start over as many times as needed, wherever we find ourselves in that moment of awakening.

Finding others who are on the same path can be a light for us when we lose our way. You may find a teacher, a group, a sangha, or perhaps a couple of friends who are interested in this reciprocally supportive arrangement. *In our Thursday morning sangha at Cancer Wellness at Piedmont Hospital, many of the participants have verbalized that they were not "group joiners" prior to being diagnosed with cancer, but that they now are so grateful they took a chance and became a part of this community. We each wear beaded mindfulness bracelets to remind us of our intentions, our practice, and enduring connection, wherever we are. One sangha member, Fran, surprised us with a generous and delightful gift, a beautiful sangha boat. We use it as a visual reminder that we are all in this boat together, mutually supportive, loving,*
and loved.

Self-Reflection

What are your patterns (internally and externally) when you lose your way?

What fears keep you from reaching out for support?

In what ways would it benefit you to reach out for support?

Practice

Brainstorm a list of possibilities that would help you gain support. Make a call or take a step in that direction.

26

A Call To Action

"All that is necessary for the triumph of evil is that good men do nothing."
-Edmund Burke

We each have the power to influence the world around us, to make it a better place, and to help heal suffering. Researchers have often asserted that we are biologically wired for competition, and yet, scientists are now finding that we are wired for cooperation and collaboration. *We (Angela and Dennis) recently watched the inspiring documentary "I AM" directed by Tom Shadyac, and learned more about the science behind our innate behavior and instincts.*

Berkeley psychology professor Dr. Dascher Keltner asserts that we are actually wired for care, compassion, and connection. In fact, the scientists in this film (I AM) mention that Darwin used the word "love" ninety-three times in his work The Descent of Man (1871) and "survival of the fittest" only twice. In fact, many cultures even perceive extreme competitiveness as a type of mental illness. Perhaps love is more of a guiding force in our survival than we once thought. Scientists at the Heartmath research lab have found that the heart actually gives more information to the brain than the brain to the heart. The benefits of listening to our hearts are being scientifically validated.

Scientists once believed that the world was flat and that to propose otherwise was actually a crime. The researchers in this documentary believe that modern science is finally proving what mystics have suggested through the ages. Through fields like quantum physics and quantum mechanics, much is being discovered about the power and influence of unseen energy fields, collective consciousness, and the power of the loving heart.

As Bodhisattvas, we each can commit to doing our parts to improve the world. As Marianne Williamson writes in her poem "Our Deepest Fear" (1996), "And as we let our own light shine, we unconsciously give other people the permission to do the same." As we awaken and have the courage to keep our own hearts open, the ripple effects of healing expand to others. As we purify our internal being with mindful practice, we become more clear and better able to let our light radiate brightly. Many of us are waiting for someone else to take the reins, similar to a theory in psychology called "diffused responsibility." Because there are so many of us, we believe that someone else will work to make things better. Actually, we are the heroes we have been waiting for. We are the answer. You are the answer. Each of us has our own unique talents, skills, and abilities to reduce suffering and heal our world.

The second line of the serenity prayer makes a request for "… the courage to change the things I can." Committing to help does require courage. Doing something different can be scary. We may feel incapable or awkward. We may even feel foolish or self-conscious. We may have concerns about taking on another commitment, that we may become overextended or will be unable to follow through. Some feel that they do not have anything to offer or that their contribution will not make a difference. The world's suffering is too large for any one person to solve, but if we each do our part, together, we can make an impact.

Imagine the possibilities when we each commit to helping. We have seen numerous stories in the media about what can occur when just one person makes this commitment or a small group is called to action. When you feel touched and inspired by these stories, something resonates in you that wants to be a part of this force for good. The ripple effects that emanate from one person, one idea, have profound and even limitless implications.

We can be of service to others and our world in numerous ways. Ram Dass explores this in his book How Can I Help?: Stories and Reflections on Service (1985). Our natural state is that of wanting to help. Pay attention to what arises in you when you help someone or when you witness someone in need being helped. As previously mentioned, we have a cascade of sensations mentally, emotionally, and physically, in response to helping.

You may choose to join a group that helps in a way close to your heart. Or you may choose to perform one random act of kindness each day. Hunkering down with the attitude of "me and mine" is no longer an option if we are to survive and thrive. In addition, you may offer prayer and metta to those who are suffering. You may make a commitment to be kinder, calmer, more open and grounded today. So many possibilities are available for you to participate in the healing and transformation of our world.

At the end of her poem "Summer Day," (1992), Mary Oliver asks "Tell me, what is it you plan to do with your one wild and precious life?" Consider this and how you can make a difference, for you and your loved ones, for humanity and the planet. How are you called to action?

Self-Reflection

In what ways would you like to help?

What blocks you from helping?

What unique gifts do you possess; special qualities that others have pointed out to you? How can you express these characteristics to influence the world around you?

Practice

Choose one activity this week as your call to action. Take a small step. See how it feels. You may change it or add to it. Just make the commitment to begin.

27

Practices

The benefits of these practices include, but are not limited to: enhanced immune functioning, reduced inflammation in the body, improved depression and anxiety symptoms, improved stress management, regulated blood pressure and sleep patterns, pain reduction, and improved ability to manage chronic pain, and better relaxation. The mindfulness research of Dr. John Kabat-Zinn et al., at University of Massachusetts Medical School, has documented "consistent, reliable, and reproducible demonstrations of major and clinically relevant reductions in medical and psychological symptoms across a wide range of medical diagnoses."

Sitting Meditation

Sitting Meditation, the most widely known of these practices, is central to mindfulness. Many people feel daunted when they consider meditation practice. They don't know where to begin, and whether they are doing it "right." Below are some tips to get started:

Find a quiet place where you will not be disturbed.

You may sit on a chair or on the floor. When sitting on the floor, we encourage using a zafu and zabuton to support your posture. You may also lie down in savasana (corpse pose). However, many people have difficulty staying awake in this pose. The goal is calm awareness, which hovers just above the dream/sleep phase of consciousness. If you find that you slip into sleep, it will be better for you to sit during meditation.

Initially, practice in the morning to set the tone for your day. When we wait until later in the day, unplanned interruptions and a frenzied schedule can thwart our intention to practice.

Try to practice in the same place at the same time each day.

Use a gentle-sounding timer so you don't worry about time.

Start in small increments, perhaps five minutes initially. If five minutes feels overwhelming, reduce it to two minutes. It is better to do "a little a lot than a lot a little" – short sessions more often, so you will reap the benefits as described above. You are also establishing a habit. We find that the more you practice, the more you want to practice. One teacher, approaches her practice as a love affair rather than a discipline. In love, we can't wait to connect with the object of our affection. We love the way it makes us feel, and we recognize the value.

The way we relate to anything alters how we approach it. Have you ever felt that you "should" call a friend? Or that you "can't wait" to talk to your friend? The difference in those attitudes can be similar to how you approach meditation. Remind yourself that this practice is a friend with many benefits, a friend that helps you to feel well and supports you unconditionally. Once you feel grounded in the initial time set for practice, increase it by five minutes.

Initially, you may find it easier to practice with a guided CD. We have created a guided meditation CD, and we list other recommendations at the end of this book.

As teachers, we are often asked about whether music (ambient or otherwise) should be used in the background during meditation. Our answer is no. The egoic mind wishes to be entertained at all times and rebels at the notion of silence. Naturally, we look for ways to make ourselves comfortable in stillness, whether it is using music or simply fantasizing. But learning to sit in silence sets a strong foundation for practice.

Ritualizing may serve as a cue to stabilize and deepen your practice. You may want to use a mediation shawl, incense, or a candle. You may want to read an inspirational passage, use a mantra or sing a chant, create an altar, or use mala beads. These rituals signal your mind/body that it is time to meditate. As a bridge to quiet the mind, you also may want to spend time doing mindful yoga or mindful walking before sitting in meditation. After meditation, you may choose to sip some tea, gaze out the window, or write in a journal, taking a few moments to be with yourself rather than jumping back into the stream of activity right away.

Posture: Consider the image of a mountain, strong and grounded. You should feel stabilized in your posture, sitting up tall and graceful, easy, open and relaxed...not too tight and not too loose. If you are on a chair, feet are flat on the floor with knees open. Spine is straight, shoulders rolled back and down to open the chest...arms are resting by your sides with your hands on your lap. See "Hand Mudras" section below for ways to place the hands. Soften the belly and the front of your throat. Close your eyes or avert them to the floor. If you are sitting on the floor, you may choose to sit in sukasana (cross-legged position), or cobbler (soles of feet together with knees outward) or diamond (loose shape of the legs) or any variation of these. You should not be in any pain or discomfort. Again, find the form of a mountain. You may also choose savasana (corpse pose) if lying down does not make you sleepy. In this pose, lay your arms open with palms up and legs apart, feet splayed away from one another. Be sure that your back is comfortably supported and that your spine is straight.

Find your breath. Notice your breath as it enters and leaves your body. Allow your mind to rest in the breath. Ride the waves of inhalation and exhalation. When your mind begins to wander into words or images (monkey mind), simply say "thinking" or "later" to yourself, and gently bring your awareness back to the breath (as many times as it wanders). Focus on the breath. As you practice more, you may drop into pure awareness, where you are not focused on the breath or anything else. The more you practice, the more you will find yourself in this place, and the longer you can reside there. There are many levels of pure awareness. References at the end of the book provide you with further information.

When you are ready to end your meditation, begin by wiggling your fingers and toes, easing your way back. Then adjust your body and head, stretching and moving easily. When you are ready, open your eyes with soft eyes, blinking a couple of times, then bring your eyes up to the horizon.

Traditionally at the end of meditation we bring our hands into prayer pose saying the word "Namaste" to ourselves, teachers present and not present, and peers who practiced with us. Namaste is the recognition of the indwelling divine, spirit, or goodness. We bow in conjunction with this offering.

Body Scan

Assume any of the postures in sitting meditation. Some practitioners enjoy doing a body scan before sitting meditation to help them settle into their bodies and quiet their minds. This practice is slightly more active and can serve as a bridge to the deeper silence held in sitting meditation.

When you are ready to begin, find your breath and bring your awareness into your body, noticing how it feels as a whole and what it is like to be in your body. As you bring your awareness into each body part, simply notice what is arising. You may notice physical, emotional, or energetic sensations. Just notice, without running a storyline. Gently bring your awareness down to your toes, then move upward into your feet, each part of your legs (either together or separate), into your pelvis, hips, and backside, up into your lower torso, then your upper torso, down to your fingers and hands and up and across your arms (either together or separate), into your throat and neck, and up into your head. Now allow your mindful awareness to expand across the entirety of your body, permitting it to rest in your body, and letting your body rest in that awareness. Notice what it feels like to be in your body with a gentle and kind awareness. Breathe in compassion and loving-kindness for your body and yourself. Breathe out and let go. Do this a few times.

When you are ready, you may proceed to sitting meditation or you may bring yourself back into the room as described in the above section.

Body scan can be done as slowly or quickly as you like. We encourage students to vary the time. If you are in the middle of your day and have only a couple of minutes, a brief body scan

can be used to quickly refresh and restore. If you have more time, the body scan can be used from ten minutes to an hour. You may choose to focus on the nuances of your body when time permits. For example, you may choose to scan each finger on one hand before moving to the next body part, or you may focus on places that do not get much attention, like the backs of your knees, your armpits, and your collarbone. You may choose to focus your awareness internally into the muscles, bones, organs, and even the cells. You may choose variations of the body scan like bringing the energy of a smile to each body part as you scan it or sending gratitude or a warm healing energy, noticing what arises as you do so. The Buddha suggested that if we can master our bodies, we can achieve enlightenment.

Hand Mudras

There are literally thousands of hand mudras. We use hand mudras to evoke certain states within the mind/heart/body/spirit. While some mudras involve the entire body, most are performed with the hands and fingers. A brain research paper published in the National Academy of Sciences in November 2009, demonstrated that hand gestures stimulate the same regions of the brain as language. We suggest three basic mudras here. For more, refer to the references at the end of the book.

1 – Palms face down on thighs – grounding

2 – Palms facing upward on thighs – open and receptive

3 -- Palm in palm with thumbs touching – internal integration

Try each of them at least once. Most people find that different days call for different mudras.

Mindful Yoga

We practice yoga like we live our lives. For some of us, this means giving up at the first sign of trouble. For others, it means being competitive, soliciting attention, or striving for perfection. Mindful yoga brings calm awareness as we move into each posture, noticing what is arising mentally, emotionally, spiritually, and physically, without grasping or resisting. These days, many yoga classes focus on athleticism, which can be ego-driven and ego-reinforcing, often overlooking meditative awareness, the essential focus on the present moment. In his book Mindful Yoga: The Awakened Union of Breath, Body and Mind (2004), Frank Jude Boccio reminds us that yoga enhances meditation, and meditation augments yoga.

Mindful yoga is a type of hatha yoga accessible to anyone regardless of age, size, or ability. In addition to the research listed at the beginning of this chapter, yoga also increases circulation, improves fatigue symptoms, improves balance, detoxifies the body, relieves hot flashes, builds strength and flexibility, and lubricates joints.

Metta Practice

In Sanskrit, "metta" means loving-kindness. In metta practice, we send loving-kindness to ourselves and others.

Assume the posture of meditation as described above, then bring your awareness to your heart, the center of your loving-kindness, your "bodhichitta" – your tender spot. As you bring mindful awareness to your heart, to the organic internal goodness that is there, feel the energy of loving-kindness begin to expand, growing warmer and stronger. You may choose to bring your hand to your heart.

First, bring yourself to mind, seeing yourself clearly, in all your humanity, in all your wonderful-ness and not so wonderful-ness, holding all of who you are in warmth and tenderness, opening your heart to yourself. Now offer metta to yourself:

May I be filled with loving-kindness.

May I be held in loving-kindness.

May I be free from suffering.

May I know great joy and deep and abiding peace.

May I awaken and be free.

Allow the warmth of these blessings to penetrate your being, down to the cellular level, embodying the love you have for yourself. Many people report resistance to offering themselves loving-kindness. Most of us were not taught to do so. Some even claim feeling self-indulgent and awkward. Some master teachers have spent months working on this before they could allow self-love and self-compassion to penetrate in a deep and abiding way. If we cannot truly love ourselves, we cannot love others in a clean, pure way either. If you find difficulty with metta for yourself, we suggest you practice this daily, not moving further, until you can embrace yourself with unconditional love and acceptance.

After we offer metta to ourselves, we offer it to a benefactor, someone who has helped us along the way, in a big or small way. Bring this person to your mind's eye, imagining where they might be in this moment, knowing that when they helped you, they were in a place of strength, but that they, too, have vulnerabilities. As you are able to see them in their fullness, offer the blessings of metta.

Breathe in and breathe out.

Now bring to mind a loved one, someone with whom you are not having any difficulties today. This person should evoke "big love" in your heart. Imagine where they might be, and offer them the blessings of metta.

Breathe in and breathe out.

Next bring to mind a neutral person, someone you do not know well or with whom you do not have a strong positive or negative emotional charge. See this person as clearly as possible in your mind's eye, and imagine where they might be in this moment. Realize that this person, like you and your loved ones, has experienced the 10,000 joys and the 10,000 sorrows and wants to find peace and happiness in this life. Now offer the blessings of metta to this brother or sister in humanity.

Breathe in and breathe out.

Now bring to mind a difficult person, someone with whom you are struggling or having conflict. Initially, choose someone causing only slight distress to you. As you practice, you strengthen this muscle and can begin offering metta to those who cause you greater distress. As you bring this person to your mind's eye, notice any feelings of resistance, anger, or anxiety, and hold yourself and these feelings in the warmth and tenderness of loving-kindness. Realize that, although this person has acted in ways you do not prefer or has caused you harm, he or she has struggled in ways that you will never know. They, too, have experienced the 10,000 joys and 10,000 sorrows. As discussed previously, it is skillful to recognize the larger context in which undesirable behaviors arise. Consider what could have transpired to elicit such behavior. This does not mean that we like what the person has done or that we agree with it. Imagine where this person might be in this moment as you offer the blessings of metta.

Breathe in and breathe out.

Now offer metta to all living beings everywhere. As you imagine doing this, feel the energy of loving-kindness growing even stronger and moving out from your heart to those around you, doing its good and perfect healing work. You may sense it encompassing the building you are in, moving down the streets of your community, across the state, the country and eventually the world.

Breathe in and breathe out.

When you are ready, allow yourself to slowly return to the room as described above.

The Buddha taught that if we were truly enlightened, we would love everyone equally – our loved ones, neutral and difficult persons, even ourselves. We suggest some traditional phrases in the above practice. You can use any phrases that feel right for you. Here are some that may appeal to you:

May you live with ease.

May you have good health.

May you be well.

May you be at peace.

You may also offer these blessings of metta informally as you go about your day. *We (Angela and Dennis) often offer metta to many with whom we cross paths, in the grocery store, walking in the park, and elsewhere. Sometimes we offer it in the moment to those we find difficult.* As you offer metta, notice any shifts it evokes in you.

Metta practice shifts our perspective, our being so caught up in ourselves - opening our hearts and creating more spaciousness within and around us. Marilyn, a sangha member, misheard what was said in class one day and aptly called this practice "metta-cine," appropriately identifying the healing benefits it provides.

Mantras and Chanting

The word mantra means "mind protection" and is used in meditation to help steady and eventually clear the mind. If we focus on a quality repeatedly, it slowly begins to penetrate, allowing us to embody it on all levels. Some practitioners find using a mantra helpful at the beginning of their meditation, as well as throughout their day to focus, quiet, and calm themselves. A mantra might be a phrase or a word.

Some examples include:

"Abiding Peace."

"I am that."

"Self-compassion and self-honor."

"Peace be still and know that I am God."

You may choose to pair a mantra with the breath. For example:

Breathing in, "Calm."....Breathing out "Ease." (Thich Nhat Hanh)

Breathing in, "I quiet my mind." Breathing out, "I calm my body."

Breathing in, "I smile." Breathing out, "Letting go." (Thich Nhat Hanh)

Create a mantra that is uniquely yours. A sankalpa is a type of mantra used specifically to capture the essence of your goal, intention, or desire.

Some examples include:

"I am Love."

"I experience radiant, vibrant health."

"Unconditional self-love and self-acceptance."

You may use mantras ritually at the beginning or end of your meditation, or throughout your day.

Chanting is similar to using mantras. An ancient practice designed to help practitioners center themselves and connect with Spirit, chanting guides us into meditative awareness, an altered state of consciousness. *Chanting with Krishna Das and Deva Premal and Miten has been an enriching experience for us. Singing wholesome and nourishing phrases with hundreds of like-minded people is a soulful, transcendent experience. We (Angela and Dennis) find ourselves chanting not only before meditation practice but also as we drive, clean, shower, and go about our daily lives. This practice relaxes us, steadies us, and reminds us of our true nature.*

A few examples of chants include:

"OM" – the sound of Spirit.

"Hari Om Shiva Om" – removal of the ego.

"Om Mani Padme Hum" – Wisdom and compassion are within and accessed on this path; reportedly used by H. H. Dalai Lama in his daily practice.

"Teyata om bekanze bekanze maha bekanze radza somudghate soha" – a call to Medicine Buddha to heal us on all levels; removing the veil of illusion or separation from Spirit.

These examples are in the traditional Sanskrit. English-language songs can be a type of chant as well. For example, "This little light of mine" can be considered a chant, focusing on wholesome and nourishing qualities. Some practitioners use chanting as their central practice while others use it as an adjunct to meditation and yoga. In his book, Chants of a Lifetime: Searching for a Heart of Gold (2010), Krishna Das writes that as we repeat these chants, "The Presence that lives within us – the Presence that lives within our own hearts, our own true nature – reveals itself." He asserts that chanting "…wakes us up and shows us our own beauty." Chanting is a path to reduce our self-imposed suffering, to remove the veil of illusion, to connect with Spirit, and to remember who we really are.

References at the end of the book provide you with further information on chanting.

Mindful Eating

You can bring mindfulness to every aspect of your life, including eating. We often approach our food and drink from a place of stress, fatigue, or emotional discomfort. At times, we are not present with our food or the process of eating. We may use food and drink to rest, calm, or disconnect. This leads to a variety of problems in our culture including eating disorders, obesity, unresolved issues, and other health problems.

Author and speaker Geneen Roth is an expert on mindful eating and has written numerous books and articles, listed at the end of the book. In these books she explains the process of trying to get our needs met through food. She offers insightful strategies for creating a healthy relationship with food.

Some tips for mindful eating:

- Take a moment of gratitude for all those who participated in delivering the food to you.
- Consider where your food came from before you eat it and what it will do in your body once it is consumed.
- Engage all of your senses –sight, smell, touch (if appropriate), and taste.
- Be aware of your breathing and your thoughts during the meal.
- Stay present. Eat when you're eating. No television, radio, work, or reading.
- Eat in silence, or engage in mindful conversation.
- Slow down. Put your fork down between bites, and chew thoroughly.

- On a scale of 1-10, don't allow yourself to become hungrier than a 3 or more full than a 7 or 8.
- Shop and prepare for your meal mindfully.
- Savor each bite. Allow yourself to enjoy the fullness of the experience.
- Create a pleasant environment with dishware you find pleasing, candles, etc.
- Notice how you feel throughout the meal, and stop eating when your level of fullness reaches a 7 or 8.

When we (Angela and Dennis) lead a mindfulness retreat, we often direct participants to eat in silence, mindfully, as a group, practicing shared solitude. Once participants get past the resistance and unfamiliarity of mindful eating, most find they love it. We suggest our students have one mindful meal a week. If they do well, we encourage them to do it more often. Mindful eating sends a message of love to our bodies.

Mindful Walking

In his book Peace is Every Step (1992), the venerable Zen master Thich Nhat Hanh describes this practice as "...allowing your feet to kiss Mother Earth with each step." He encourages the monks within his monastery to practice walking meditation regularly. You can practice this anywhere, from an ashram to the park. Initially, start slowly. Once you feel grounded in the practice, increase your pace. Bring your mindful awareness to your breath and body, noticing how you feel internally with each step, letting go of any storylines. You may choose to avert your eyes initially, as the world around you may be too distracting. With practice, you can bring your awareness to both your external and internal environments, becoming present and aware of sights and sounds, letting go of any storylines. If you notice monkey mind arising, bring your awareness back to your breath and the body.

You may choose to coordinate your breath with the steps, breathing in for a few steps and breathing out for a few steps. This pairing can help you find your rhythm. You may also choose to pair a word or mantra with your steps.

Notice how your body feels during your walk. Notice the sensations of the foot rolling on the ground, the way you are holding your belly, the carriage of your shoulders. To integrate this practice fully into your life, walk mindfully once a day, perhaps each time you go to your car. Eventually, you can expand this practice to include mindful movement, being present and aware as you reach for a glass or turn on your computer. As you become more comfortable, you can move at a faster pace while maintaining meditative awareness.

Guided Meditations

Guided meditations can be helpful when working on specific issues like forgiveness, anger, grief, or stress. Bringing a meditative awareness to these issues can help us heal, release, and transform them. During such internal work, we suggest keeping a journal nearby. You may find it beneficial to write your feelings, thoughts, and experiences before and after a guided meditation. This work usually requires returning to various topics more than once. Each time you return to a topic, you work at a deeper level, creating more grounded and enduring internal shifts.

A CD of guided meditations, CALM, is available on our blog and website.

References

References

Barks, Coleman. *The Essential Rumi.* San Francisco, CA: HarperOne, 2004.

Bennett, Mary, et al. *"The effect of mirthful laughter on stress and natural killer cell activity."* Alternative Therapies in Health and Medicine, 9, 2003.

Bennett-Goleman, Tara. *Emotional Alchemy: How the Mind Can Heal the Heart.* New York: Three Rivers, 2002.

Berk, Lee et al. *"Modulation of neuroimmune parameters during the eustress of humor-associated mirthful laughter."* Alternative Therapies in Health and Medicine, 7, 2001.

Boccio, Frank Jude and Georg Feuerstein. *Mindfulness Yoga: The Awakened Union of Breath, Body and Mind.* Boston: Wisdom Publications, 2004.

Boorstein, Sylvia. *Happiness is an Inside Job: Practicing for a Joyful Life.* New York: Ballantine Books, 2007.

Brefczynski-Lewis, Julie et al. *"Meditation and Brain Imaging."* Handbook of Integrative Clinical Psychology, Psychiatry, and Behavioral Medicine, 2007.

Chodron, Pema. *Start Where You Are: A Guide to Compassionate Living.* Boston: Shambhala, 2001.

Chodron, Pema. *The Wisdom of No Escape.* Boston: Shambhala, 2001.

Chodron, Pema. *Comfortable With Uncertainty: 108 Teaching on Cultivating Fearlessness.* Boston: Shambhala, 2002.

Chodron, Pema. *Don't Bite the Hook: Finding Freedom from Anger, Resentment, and Other Destructive Emotions.* San Francisco, CA: Shambhala Audio, 2007.

Chodron, Pema. *Unconditional Confidence: Instructions for Meeting Any Experience with Trust and Courage.* Louisville, CO: Sounds True, 2009.

Chodron, Pema. *From Fear to Fearlessness.* Louisville, CO: Sounds True, 2003.

Creswell, J. D. et al. *"Neural correlates of dispositional mindfulness during affect labeling."* Psychosomatic Medicine, 69, 560-565.

Darwin, Charles. *The Descent of Man.* London: John Murray, 1871.

Dass, Ram and Paul Gorman. *How Can I Help? Stories and Reflection on Service.* New York: Knopf, 1985.

Davidson, Richard and Antoine Lutz. *"Buddha's Brain: Neuroplasticity and Meditation."* IEEE Signal Process Magazine. 2008 January 1; 25(1): 176–174.

Davidson, R.J., Kabat-Zinn, J. et al. *"Alterations in brain and immune function produced by mindfulness meditation."* Psychosomatic Medicine, 2003.

Dickens, Charles, *A Christmas Carol.* London: Chapmen & Hall, 1843.

Doidge, Norman. *The Brain That Changes Itself.* New York: Viking Adult, 2007.

Dreamer, Oriah M. *The Invitation.* San Francisco: HarperOne, 1999. By Oriah from her book, THE INVITATION (c)1999. Published by HarperONE, San Francisco. All rights reserved. Presented with permission of the author. www.oriah.org.

Dyer, Wayne. *The Power of Intention.* Carlsbad, CA: Hay House, 2004.

Emmons, Robert. *Thanks!: How the New Science of Gratitude Can Make You Happier.* Boston: Houghton Mifflin Harcourt, 2007.

Emoto, Masaru. *The Hidden Messages in Water.* Hillsboro, OR: Beyond Words, 2004.

Fowler, James and Nicholas Christakis. *"Dynamic Spread of Happiness in a Large Social Network: Longitudinal Analysis over 20 Years in the Framingham Heart Study."* BMJ 337:a2338., 2008.

Fox, John. *Poetic Medicine: The Healing Art of Poem-Making.* New York: Tarcher, 1997.

Fox, John. *Finding What You Didn't Lose: Expressing Your Creativity Through Poem-Making.* New York: Tarcher, 1995.

Gibran, Khalil. *The Prophet.* New York: A.A. Knopf, 1923.

Gilbert, Elizabeth. *Eat, Pray, Love: One Woman's Search for Everything Across Italy, India and Indonesia.* New York: Penguin, 2007.

Grandey, Alicia. *"Emotion Regulation in the Workplace: A New Way to Conceptualize Emotional Labor."* Journal of Occupational Health Psychology. January, 2000.

Hanh, Thich Nhat. *Savor: Mindful Eating, Mindful Life.* San Francisco, CA: HarperOne, 2010.

Hanh, Thich Nhat. *Mindfulness and Psychotherapy.* Louisville, CO: Sounds True, 2006.

Hawkins, David. *Power vs. Force: The Hidden Determinants of Human Behavior.* Carlsbad, CA: Hay House, 2002.

Kabat-Zinn, Jon. *Coming To Our Senses.* New York: Hyperion, 2005.

Kabat-Zinn, Jon. *Full Catastrophe Living.* Concord, CA: Delta, 1990.

Kabat-Zinn, Jon el al. *"The clinical use of mindfulness meditation for the self-regulation of chronic pain."* Journal of Behavioral. Medicine. (1985) 8:163-190.

Kabat-Zinn, Jon et al. *"Effectiveness of a meditation-based stress reduction program in the treatment of anxiety disorders."* American Journal of Psychiatry (1992) 149:936-943.

Kabat-Zinn, Jon *"Psychosocial Factors in Coronary Heart Disease: Their Importance and Management."* In *Prevention of Coronary_Heart Disease*, Boston: Little Brown, 1993, pp. 299-333.

Kabat-Zinn, Jon et al. *"Influence of a mindfulness-based stress reduction intervention on rates of skin clearing in patients with moderate to severe psoriasis undergoing phototherapy (UVB) and photochemotherapy (PUVA)."* Psychosomatic Medicine (1998) 60:625-632.

Keltner, Dascher. *Born to Be Good: The Science of a Meaningful Life.* New York: W. W. Norton & Company, 2009.

Keltner, Dascher. *"The Compassionate Instinct: A Darwinian Tale of the Survival of the Kindest."* Meng-Wu Lecture Series, University of California/Berkeley, 2011.

Kinnell, Galway. "*St. Francis and the Sow*" from *Three Books.* Boston: Houghton Mifflin, 2002.

Kornfied, Jack. *The Wise Heart: A Guide to the Universal Teachings of Buddhist Psychology.* New York: Bantam, 2008.

Lieberman, Matthew et al. *"Subjective responses to emotional stimuli during labeling, reappraisal, and distraction."* Emotion, 11, 468-480.

Luks, Allan and Peggy Payne. *The Healing Power of Doing Good.* Bloomington, IN: iUniverse 2001.

Miller, Andrea. *Real People, Real Practice.* Shambhala Sun, January 2011, pp. 52-55.
Moffit, Phillip. *Dancing with Life: Buddhist Insights for Finding Meaning and Joy in the Face of Suffering.* Emmaus, PA: Rodale, 2008.

Multiple Sources. *Learning To Forgive May Improve Well-Being.* Science Daily, January, 2008.

Northrup, Christiane. *The Wisdom of Menopause: Creating Physical and Emotional Health and Healing During the Change.* New York: Bantam, 2003.

Oliver, Mary. *"The Summer Day"* from *The Truro Bear and Other Adventures: Poems and Essays*. Boston: Beacon Press, 2008.

Pert, Candace. *Molecules Of Emotion: The Science Behind Mind-Body Medicine.* New York: Simon & Schuster, 1999.

Post, Stephen and Jill Neimark. *Why Bad Things Happen to Good People.* New York: Bantam Dell, 2007.

Raison, Charles et al. *"Effect of Compassion Meditation on Neuroendocrine Innate Immune and Behavioral Responses to Psychosocial Stress."* Psychoneuroendocrinology, January 2009.

Roth, Geneen. *Feeding the Hungry Heart: The Experience of Compulsive Eating.* New York: Plume, 1993.

Roth, Geneen. *Lost and Found: Unexpected Revelations About Food and Money.* New York: Viking Adult, 2011.

Rowe-Ward, Peggy and Larry Ward. *Love's Garden: A Guide To Mindful Relationships.* Berkeley, CA: Parallax Press, 2008.

Salzberg, Sharon. *Lovingkindness: The Revolutionary Art of Happiness.* Boston: Shambhala, 1997.

Satchidananda, Sri Swami. *The Yoga Sutras of Patanjali: Commentary on the Raja Yoga Sutras.* Buckingham, VA: Integral Yoga Publications, 1990.
Siegel, Daniel and Jack Kornfield. *Mindfulness and the Brain: A Professional Training in the Science and Practice of Meditative Awareness.* Louisville, CO: Sounds True, 2010.

Siegel, Daniel. *The Mindful Brain: Reflection and Attunement in the Cultivation of Well-Being*, New York: W. W. Norton & Company, 2007.

Sifneos, Peter. "*Alexithymia: past and present.*" American Journal Psychiatry 153:137-142, 1996.

Smookler, Elaine, et al., "*Make Me One With Everything.*" Bhuddha*dharma,* Summer 2011.

Stockdale, Brenda. *You Can Beat the Odds: The Surprising Factors Behind Chronic Illness and Cancer.* Boulder, CO: Sentient Publications, 2009.

Thoreau, Henry David. *Walden.* London: George Routledge & Sons, 1904.

Waldeck, Nancy. *Taste and Savor: Delicious, Healthy Recipes & Tasty Wine Tips.* 2010.

Whitworth, Judith et al. "*Cushing, Cortisol, and Cardiovascular Disease.*" Hypertension. 2000; 36:912.

Williamson, Marianne. *The Gift of Change: Spiritual Guidance for a Radically New Life.* New York: HarperOne, 2006.

Williamson, Marianne. *A Return To Love: Reflections on the Principles of "A Course in Miracles."* New York: Harper Collins, 1996.

Worthington, Jr., Everett. *Forgiveness and Reconciliation: Theory and Application.* Kentucky: Routledge, 2006.

Uher, Tomas. "*Alexithymia And Immune Dysregulation: A Critical Review.*" Activitas Nervosa Superior, March 2010.

Recommended Resources

Recommended Resources

Books

Austin, James – Zen and the Brain: Toward an Understanding of Meditation and Consciousness, 1999

Barks, Coleman and Hudson Smith - The Essential Rumi, 2004

Boccio, Frank Jude and Georg Feuerstein, – Mindfulness Yoga: The Awakened Union of Breath, Body, and Mind, 2004

Brach, Tara – Radical Acceptance: Embracing Your Life With the Heart of a Buddha, 2008

Boorstein, Sylvia – Happiness Is an Inside Job: Practicing for a Joyful Life, 2008

Boorstein, Sylvia – Pay Attention, for Goodness' Sake: The Buddhist Path of Kindness, 2003

Chodron, Pema – Comfortable with Uncertainty: 108 Teachings on Cultivating Fearlessness and Compassion, 2008

Chodron, Pema - The Wisdom of No Escape: And the Path of Loving-Kindness, 2008

Chodron, Pema – Practicing Peace in Times of War, 2007

Chodron, Pema – When Things Fall Apart: Heart Advice for Difficult Times, 2000

Chodron, Pema – No Time to Lose: A Timely Guide to the Way of the Bodhisattva, 2007

Cope, Stephen – Yoga and the Quest for the True Self, 2000

Das, Krishna – Chants of a Lifetime, 2010

Dass, Ram – Remember, Be Here Now, 1971

Dass, Ram and Paul Gorman – How Can I Help? Stories and Reflection on Service, 1985

Fox, John - Poetic Medicine: The Healing Art of Poem-Making, 1997

Fox, John - Finding What You Didn't Lose: Expressing Your and Creativity Through Poem-Making, 1997

Goldstein, Joseph – Insight Meditation: The Practice of Freedom, 2003

Hanh, Thich Nhat – Anger, 2002

Hanh, Thich Nhat – Peace Is Every Step: The Path of Mindfulness in Everyday Life, 1992

Hanh, Thich Nhat – Living Buddha, Living Christ, 2007

Hanh, Thich, Nhat with Dr. Lillian Cheung - Savor: Mindful Eating, Mindful Life, 2011

Hirschi, Gertrud – Mudras: Yoga in Your Hands, 2000

Kabat-Zinn, Jon – Full Catastrophe Living: Using the Wisdom of Your Body and Mind to Face Stress, Pain, and Illness, 1990

Kabat-Zinn, Jon – Coming to Our Senses: Healing Ourselves and the World Through Mindfulness, 2006

Kabat-Zinn, Jon - Wherever You Go, There You Are, 2005

Kornfield, Jack – The Wise Heart, 2009

Kornfield, Jack – After the Ecstasy, the Laundry: How the Heart Grows Wise On The Spiritual Path, 2001

Lama, Dalai – The Art of Happiness, 2009

Lama, Dalai – How to See Yourself as You Really Are, 2007

Larkin, Geri – Stumbling toward Enlightenment, 2008

Larkin, Geri – The Chocolate Cake Sutra: Ingredients for a Sweet Life, 2007

Levine, Stephen – Healing Into Life and Death, 1989

Levine, Stephen and Ondrea – Embracing the Beloved: Relationship as a Path of Awakening, 1996

Levine, Stephen – A Gradual Awakening, 1989

Levine, Stephen - Turning Toward the Mystery: A Seeker's Journey, 2003

Louden, Jennifer. The Life Organizer: A Woman's Guide to a Mindful Year, 2007

Merullo, Roland – Breakfast with Buddha, 2008

Moffit, Phillip – Dancing with Life: Buddhist Insights for Finding Meaning and Joy in the Face of Suffering, 2008

Osborne, Arthur- Ramana Maharshi and the Path of Self-Knowledge, 2006

Roth, Geneen – Feeding the Hungry Heart: The Experience of Compulsive Eating, 1993

Roth, Geneen – When Food Is Love: Exploring the Relationship Between Eating and Intimacy, 1992

Roth, Geneen – Women Food and God: An Unexpected Path to Almost Everything, 2011

Rowe-Ward, Peggy and Larry – Love's Garden: A Guide to Mindful Relationships, 2008

Rinpoche, Sogyal; Gaffney, Patrick and Andrew Harvey – The Tibetan Book of Living and Dying, 1994

Salzberg, Sharon – Lovingkindness: The Revolutionary Art of Happiness (Shambhala Classics), 2002

Salzberg, Sharon – Faith: Trusting Your Own Deepest Experience, 2003

Surya Das, Lama – Awakening the Buddha Within: Tibetan Wisdom for the Western World, 1998

Surya Das, Lama – Buddha Is as Buddha Does: The Ten Original Practices for Enlightened Living, 2008

Thoreau, Henry David, Emerson, Ralph Waldo - The Complete Works of Ralph Waldo Emerson & Henry David Thoreau, 2008

Tolle, Eckhart – The Power of Now: A Guide to Spiritual Enlightenment, 2004

Tolle, Eckhart – A New Earth: Awakening to Your Life's Purpose, 2008

Waldeck, Nancy - Taste and Savor: Delicious, Healthy Recipes & Tasty Wine Tips, 2010

Welwood, John – Toward a Psychology of Awakening: Buddhism, Psychotherapy, and the Path of Personal and Spiritual Transformation, 2002

Wilber, Ken – One Taste: Daily Reflections on Integral Spirituality, 2000

Wilber, Ken and Treya Wilber– Grace and Grit: Spirituality and Healing in the Life and Death of Treya Killam Wilber, 2001

Williamson, Marianne – A Return to Love: Reflections on the Principles of A Course in Miracles, 1990

Williamson, Marianne – The Gift of Change, 2006

Williamson, Marianne – Everyday Grace, 2004

Yogananda, Paramahansa – Autobiography of a Yogi, 2000

Poetry

Angelou, Maya. The Complete Collected Poems of Maya Angelou. 1994

Barks, Coleman and Huston Smith – The Essential Rumi, 2004

Barks, Coleman – Rumi: The Book of Love: Poems of Ecstasy and Longing, 2003

Fox, John – Poetic Medicine, The Healing Art of Poem-Making, 1997

Hafiz and Ladinsky, Daniel – I Heard God Laughing: Poems of Hope and Joy, 2006

Hafiz, and Daniel Ladinsky – The Gift, 1999

Housden, Roger - Dancing with Joy: 99 Poems, 2007

Levine, Stephen – Breaking the Drought: Visions of Grace, 2007

Oliver, Mary – The Truro Bear and Other Adventures: Poems and Essays, 2008

Rumi, Jalal Al-Din; Barks, Coleman; Green, Michael – The Illuminated Rumi, 1997

Audio

Note: Many of the books listed above are also available in audio book format.

Soundstrue.com – for a wide variety of selections

Hanh, Thich Nhat – Mindfulness and Psychotherapy, 2006

Chodron, Pema – Don't Bite the Hook: Finding Freedom from Anger, Resentment, and Other Destructive Emotions: Library Edition, 2008

Chodron, Pema – Pure Meditation, 2001

Chodron, Pema – From Fear to Fearlessness, 2008

Chodron, Pema – Getting Unstuck, 2005

Chodron, Pema – Unconditional Confidence, 2010

Tolle, Eckhart – Living a Life of Inner Peace, 2004

Siegel, Dan; Kornfield, Jack – Mindfulness and the Brain: A Professional Training in the Science and Practice of Meditative Awareness, 2010

Kornfield, Jack - Guided Meditations for Difficult Times: A Lamp in the Darkness, 2010

Kornfield, Jack - Guided Meditation: Six Essential Practices to Cultivate Love, Awareness, and Wisdom, 2007

Kabat-Zinn, Jon - Mindfulness for Beginners, (2007)

Weil, Andrew and Jon Kabat-Zinn - Meditation for Optimum Health: How to Use Mindfulness and Breathing to Heal, 2001

Links We Love

www.allthingsintegrative.com Buttimer Integrative Health & Wellness

www.piedmontcancer.org Cancer Wellness at Piedmont

www.poeticmedicine.org John Fox

www.tasteandsavor.com Nancy Waldeck

www.hobbsacupuncture.com David Hobbs

www.shinedesignstudios.com Nancy Sherrill

www.wellnessandwritingconnections.com John Evans

www.lotusinstitute.com Peggy and Larry Ward

www.oriahmountaindreamer.com Oriah Mountain Dreamer

www.sio.com Society of Integrative Oncology

www.volunteermatch.org

www.volunteer.com

Chanting CDs

Breezan, Jennifer - Returning

Das, Krishna – The Best of Krishna Das, Flow of Grace, Door of Faith

Kaur, Snatum - Shanti

Premal, Deva and Miten – Embrace, Essence, Gayatri Mantra

Uttal, Jai – Loveland, Pranyama, Kirtan

Periodicals

Shambhala Sun

Tricycle

Yoga Journal

Retreats

Kripalu - Boston, Massachusetts

Omega - New York, New York

Southern Dharma - North Carolina

Spirit Rock – Woodacre, California

Documentary

Shadyac, Tom, I AM

Meditation Supplies

Dharmacrafts

Yoga Supplies

SunShine Yoga

Yoga Accessories

About Cancer Wellness at Piedmont

Each month, hundreds of cancer patients, survivors and their families look to Cancer Wellness at Piedmont for care. We offer comprehensive, complimentary service and programs to anyone affected by cancer at any phase in his or her cancer journey. Professionally-led programs include education, relaxation and stress reduction, movement and exercise, expressive arts, meditation, support groups, individual nutritional and psychological counseling, cooking demos and social events.

Our mission is to consistently provide quality psychosocial programs as an adjunct to conventional medical care that improves quality of life and promotes health and well-being. Thanks to generous philanthropic support, Piedmont is able to offer these programs free of charge and open to anyone in greater Atlanta affected by cancer.

All programs take place at Cancer Wellness at Piedmont, located in the Piedmont Hospital Cancer Center, 1800 Howell Mill Road (Piedmont West Medical Office Park), Suite 700, Atlanta, 30318, unless otherwise noted in the class listing. Also, we realize people have good days and bad days, so registration is not required for classes unless noted. Parking is offered on-site. Please bring your parking ticket to the program facilitator for validation.

The Cancer Wellness Center is able to maintain our standard of superior care and services to the community because of the generosity of our donors. Each gift, large or small, is appreciated and is for the exclusive benefit of those families on a journey with cancer. If you are interested in supporting our mission, please contact Piedmont Philanthropy at 404-605-2130.

For information about programs and services online, visit www.piedmontcancer.org.

About the Authors

Angela Buttimer, MS, NCC, LPC, RYT, and Dennis Buttimer, MEd, CEAP, RYT, are counselors and coaches in private practice in Atlanta, Georgia. Partners in Buttimer and Associates, LLC, their life's work is dedicated to helping others heal, approaching health and wellness from a holistic perspective – honoring the connection of mind, body, heart, and spirit. Angela and Dennis both hold master's degrees in counseling psychology and have advanced training in various areas. In their work, they blend western psychotherapy, eastern philosophy, transpersonal psychology, and metaphysical principles. They are also registered yoga and meditation teachers, offering mindfulness training, as well as yoga classes, to various segments of the community.

They write about integrative health and wellness research and strategies in their blog, www.allthingsintegrative.com. They facilitate various wellness programs at Cancer Wellness at Piedmont Hospital. They have worked extensively in corporate, higher education, hospitals, non-profit, and in the public sector, facilitating trainings on various topics. Their primary interests include mindfulness, yoga, writing, stress management, and integrative health and wellness. They are key-note speakers, retreat leaders, and workshop facilitators. To learn more, please visit their website: www.buttimer-associates.com.